Nonlinear Models of
Interacting Populations

REVIEWS OF MODERN PHYSICS MONOGRAPHS

B. N. Taylor, W. H. Parker, and D. N. Langenberg
The Fundamental Constants and Quantum
Electrodynamics, 1969

N. S. Goel, S. C. Maitra, and E. W. Montroll
On the Volterra and Other Nonlinear Models
of Interacting Populations, 1971

ON THE VOLTERRA AND OTHER

Nonlinear Models of Interacting Populations

N. S. Goel

S. C. Maitra

E. W. Montroll

Institute for Fundamental Studies
Department of Physics and Astronomy
The University of Rochester, Rochester, New York

A Reviews of Modern Physics Monograph

Academic Press / New York / London / 1971

ACADEMIC PRESS, INC.
111 Fifth Avenue, New York, New York 10003

United Kingdom Edition published by
ACADEMIC PRESS, INC. (LONDON) LTD.
Berkeley Square House, London W1X 6BA

LIBRARY OF CONGRESS CATALOG CARD NUMBER: 70-167781

Originally printed in the
REVIEWS OF MODERN PHYSICS,
Volume 43, Number 2, pp. 231-276, April 1971

*THIS SOURCE SHOULD BE USED
FOR REFERENCE CITATION*

PRINTED IN THE UNITED STATES OF AMERICA

Contents

ACKNOWLEDGMENTS vii

I. Introduction 1

II. Volterra Model 7

III. A Primitive Statistical Model of
Population Growth 23

IV. Equilibrium Theory 41

V. Time-Dependent Fluctuations in
Population 59

VI. Diversity and Stability in Ecological
Systems 77

VII. Volterra Equations with Random Rate
Constants 87

VIII. Population Growth as Birth and Death
Processes 97

IX. Time Lags in Population 101

X. Generalization of Volterra Equations . . 113

XI. Experimental Verification of Volterra's
Model 121

Appendix A. Time Averages of Various
Functions of N_i and $\dot{N}_i$ 125

Appendix B. Microcanonical Averages of
Various Functions of N_i 131

Appendix C. Canonical Averages of Various
Functions of N_i, v_i, and Their Time . . .
Derivatives 137

Appendix D. Roots of the Equation
$ze^z + \gamma = 0$, γ complex 141

References 143

Acknowledgments

N. S. Goel gratefully acknowledges several discussions with Dr. Egbert Leigh, who also introduced to him Kerner's and his own work. He also acknowledges several discussions with Dr. Robert Rosen. We thank Dr. Nira Dyn for critically reading the manuscript and making several useful remarks. The numerical calculations in Section I were carried out by Mr. Ardean Leith of The University of Rochester Computing Center, which is, in part, supported by National Science Foundation Grant GJ-828.

This research was partially supported by the U. S. Air Force Office of Scientific Research (Grant No. AF-AFOSR-1314-67) and by the Advanced Research Projects Agency of the Department of Defense, and was monitored by ONR under Contract No. N00014-67-A-0398-0005.

I. Introduction

There exist numerous examples of assemblies which consist of a number of elements that influence each other through competition or cooperation. Some important cases are: populations of various biological species; political parties; businesses; countries; coupled reacting chemical components in the atmosphere, in bodies of water, and in organisms as a whole or in part; components of the nervous system; and elementary excitations in fluids (for example, eddies in a turbulent fluid).

One can construct models of many of these assemblies, either from first principles or intuitively, for the description of the competitive or cooperative phenomena. They yield rate equations, generally nonlinear, which contain a number of rate constants which must be determined empirically or be calculated from some auxiliary equations. When the number of interacting variables is large, the rate equations may become difficult to solve and, as is the case in the application of classical mechanics to physical problems, one might not even know all the initial conditions of the problem. It is, therefore, of interest to try to develop a "statistical mechanics" for many coupled rate equations. Some important aspects of any assembly of elements which can be studied using statistical mechanics are its inherent stability, its stability relative to small changes in the rate constants, and its stability relative to the introduction of a new element. One is also interested in the basic relaxation times of the assembly.

With the currently developing interest in the investigation of social and biological mechanisms, it is of considerable importance to find a model which might be amenable to a detailed investigation. Such a model might play the same role that the harmonic oscillator or the Ising model plays in theoretical physics.

An interesting model for the interaction between a number of different biological species was introduced by Volterra a number of years ago[1] (1928, 1931, and 1937). The two-species version of the model and its similarity to autocatalytic reactions had already been discussed independently by Lotka (1910, 1920, 1956). The model was, for a while, considered as a basis for ecological processes. It was strongly criticized because certain features of ecological systems were omitted. We are under the impression that the fall from favor occurred because of general notions about the omissions and oversimplifications and not because calculations based on the model were in strong contradiction to observations. Indeed, few nontrivial deductions were made from the model since it is a nonlinear one. If the same kind of criticism had discouraged people from the investigation of models (such as the van der Waals model, the Ising model, the Lee model in quantum field theory, the Kronig–Penney model, the mass and spring model of lattice vibrations, the Heisenberg model of ferromagnetism, model of electrons imbedded in a continuous positive charge background, etc.) used in many-body physics, physicists would have never developed the intuition necessary for the understanding of the behavior of complicated real materials. The model as introduced by Volterra is described in the next section where we have also discussed the implications of the model for the two-species case. In addition we show that for the model there is a constant of motion. However, if one includes the effect that a population, surviving on limited resources, approaches saturation, there is no constant of motion. At various points in this paper and in a later one we will investigate the influence of this and various other omissions and

---

[1] An excellent English review of the original Volterra theory and its use for the interpretation of experiments involving a small number of species can be found in the book of D'Ancona (1954).

simplifications of the Volterra model. Our main aim here, however, is to consider it as one of the simplest of nonlinear competition models. Because of certain accidental aspects of the model which might not have been planned by Volterra, we will be able to carry out a program which would be desirable but not always easy to pursue in other models.

In Sec. 2 we study the population growth of a species by assuming that the effect of other species is to introduce a random function of time in the growth equation. The resulting equation has the same mathematical form as the Schrödinger and Bloch equations. That equation is solved to obtain the probability distribution $P(N, t)$ of the population as a function of time.

In Sec. 3 we discuss various necessary conditions for the existence of an equilibrium concentration of the component species. We show that a great deal can be said about this question from knowledge only of the graph which describes which species interact with each other (the "organization chart" for the ecology).

As mentioned above, in the absence of detailed information about the interaction between the species, a statistical mechanical treatment of a population is very desirable. The first statistical mechanical considerations of the Volterra model were made by Kerner (1957, 1959, 1971). His theory, though elegant, has been criticized because he has given no justification for the validity of the application of the statistical mechanics to the problem of population of interacting species. We know that, even in physics, the justification of statistical mechanics is rather tricky. Perhaps its most simple and convincing justification in that field lies in its connection with thermodynamics. No such connection, which is close to experiment, exists for the Volterra model. Kerner's treatment has also been applied to the study of an assembly of interacting biochemical reactions (Goodwin, 1963), to the nervous system (Cowan, 1968), and to a system of simultaneously growing cells (Goodwin, 1970). In these assemblies the

3

validity of statistical mechanics is also assumed. Because of the importance and simplification of a statistical treatment, we have attempted to justify it in Sec. 4. We start with the dynamics of the system described by the Volterra's equations, (sometimes with some modifications) and determine the conditions under which the results obtained by a statistical mechanical analysis are consistent with the results obtained directly from the Volterra equation. In particular, we determine under what conditions the canonical averages satisfy the equations by the time averages of arbitrary functions of a number of various species.

In Sec. 5 we discuss the stability of systems in terms of the statistical properties of their population fluctuations. We define a measure of the stability of an ecology which could be used to compare the relative stabilities of two ecologies with the same macroscopic properties.

One might expect the "rate constants" appearing in Volterra's model to be affected by changes in temperature, humidity, age distribution of various species, and other ecological factors. On this basis we assume the rate constants to be random and derive and discuss the master equation for the probability distribution of N_i's in Sec. 6. We show that the stationary population distribution is Poisson only if the variation in the rate constants is not too rapid. We also briefly outline in Sec. 7 another stochastic model for the population growth of interacting and competing species in which the equation satisfied by the probability distribution is expressed in terms of the probabilities of birth and death of the individuals.

In general, the members of the population do not react instantaneously to any change in the environment; the egg is not instantaneously converted into an adult and the prey–predator interactions do not affect the population of both the prey and the predator instantaneously. In Sec. 8 we discuss the effects of the time lags in the above processes on the behavior, in particular the stability, of the population.

In Sec. 9 we review some of the work done in recent years in an attempt to generalize and to modify the Volterra equations. These generalizations throw some light on the behavior of the population if Volterra's model is changed; also, the generalized equations may be more realistic in describing the behavior of other systems of interacting species. In the latter category, we specifically point out the nervous system, a system of biochemical oscillators, a system of growing bacterial cells, and the multimode optical maser.

In Sec. 10 we give a sampling of the experiments which throw some light on the validity of Volterra's model for two or three species and the application of statistical mechanics to many-species case within the same model.

Moderate birthrates of X_1 to
simulate fact that X_2 will find
less to feed on as X_1 increases
Slowest growing X_1 has lowest
X_2 influence

Should be able to
build in population pressure
by having subspecies act
against each other

$$\frac{dN_3}{dt} = -d_3 N_3 + \lambda_3 N_2 N_3$$

II. Volterra Model

Volterra was motivated to investigate competing species by discussions with his friend D'Ancona (1926), who made a statistical analysis of fish catches in the Adriatic. It was apparently observed that the populations of two species of fish commonly found in these catches varied with the same period, but somewhat out of phase. One of these was a species of small fish which we identify as "1," and the other was a species of a larger fish which we identify as "2." It seemed as though the large fish ate the small ones, grew, and multiplied until the population of small ones diminished to such a level that there were insufficient numbers for the survival of the large ones. As the population of large ones declined, that of the small species prospered to the degree that a larger number of large fish could be supported, etc. This qualitative mechanism was described by Volterra through the pair of equations

$$dN_1/dt = \alpha_1 N_1 - \lambda_1 N_1 N_2, \qquad (1.1a)$$

$$dN_2/dt = -\alpha_2 N_2 + \lambda_2 N_1 N_2. \qquad (1.1b)$$

The term $-\lambda_1 N_1 N_2$ represents the loss rate of small fish due to "collisions" with larger ones, and $\lambda_2 N_1 N_2$ represents the growth rate of the population of the species of larger fish through the same collisions. In this model, species 1 would grow exponentially in the absence of species 2, while species 2 would die out without the availability of 1. Lotka (1910) had independently investigated these equations in the theory of autocatalytic chemical reactions, as well as in the theory of competing species (Lotka, 1920).

7

$\beta_i = \dfrac{\text{biomass}}{\text{individual}}$

biomass transfer from j to i per unit time

The pair of equations (1.1) has been generalized by Volterra to the n-species set

$$dN_i/dt = k_i N_i + \beta_i^{-1} \sum_{j=1}^{n} a_{ij} N_i N_j. \qquad (1.2)$$

The first term describes the behavior of ith species in the absence of others; when $k_i > 0$, the ith species is postulated to grow in an exponential Malthusian manner with k_i as the "rate constant." When $k_i < 0$ and all other $N_j = 0$, the population of the ith species would die out exponentially. The quadratic terms in Eq. (1.2) describe the interaction of the ith species with all the other species. The ith term in the quadratic sum is proportional to the number of possible binary encounters $N_i N_j$ between members of the ith species and members of the jth species. The constants a_{ij} might be either positive, negative, or zero. A positive a_{ij} tells us how rapidly encounters between ith and jth species will lead to an increase in N_i; a negative a_{ij} tells how rapidly these encounters will lead to a decrease in N_i, and a zero a_{ij} simply denotes the fact that ith and jth species do not interact. If, during a collision between ith and jth species, jth species are gained, then ith species are lost. Hence a_{ij} and a_{ji} have opposite signs. The positive quantities β_i^{-1} have been named "equivalence" numbers by Volterra. During binary collisions of species i and j, the ratio of i's lost (or gained) per unit time to j's gained (or lost) is $\beta_i^{-1}/\beta_j^{-1}$. With this definition, we have

Confusing

$$a_{ij} = -a_{ji}. \qquad (1.3)$$

Except under certain conditions which we discuss below, we have

$$a_{ii} \equiv 0 \qquad \text{for all } i. \qquad (1.4)$$

We define the steady state of our assembly to be characterized by that set of populations $\{N_j\}$ for which $dN_j/dt = 0$ for all j. The quantity q_j is defined to be the value of N_j under this condition so that the defining

No. Second Law of Thermodynamics says can't be 100% efficient. Hence prey

8

equations for $\{q_i\}$ are

$$q_i[k_i\beta_i+ \sum_j a_{ij}q_j]=0. \qquad (1.5)$$

When none of the q's vanish, they satisfy

$$k_i\beta_i+ \sum_{j=1}^{n} a_{ij}q_j=0 \qquad i=1, 2, \cdots, n. \qquad (1.6)$$

It is important to note, as was first shown by Volterra, that there is a constant of motion which depends on the $\{q_j\}$ for our assembly.[2] We define

$$v_j= \log(N_j/q_j) \quad \text{or} \quad N_j=q_j \exp{(v_j)}. \qquad (1.7)$$

Clearly, as $N_j\to q_j$, $v_j\to 0$ so that v_j is a measure of the deviation from equilibrium. The rate equation (1.2) is easily expressed in terms of the v_j [by expressing $k_i\beta_i$ through Eq. (1.6)]:

$$\beta_j dv_j/dt= \sum_i a_{ji}q_i[\exp{(v_i)}-1]. \qquad (1.8)$$

If we multiply both sides of this equation by $q_j[\exp{(v_j)}-1]$ and sum over all j, we find

$$d/dt \sum_j \beta_j q_j[\exp{(v_j)}-v_j]$$

$$= \sum_{ij} a_{ji}q_i q_j[\exp{(v_i)}-1][\exp{(v_j)}-1]=0,$$

the double sum vanishing because the summand is antisymmetrical in i and j. Then, we find

$$G= \sum_j \beta_j q_j[-v_j+ \exp{(v_j)}]= \text{const} = \sum G_j \qquad (1.9a)$$

so that G is our desired constant of motion. Every individual term in G is positive since in case (a) $v_j>0$ implies $\exp{(v_j)}>v_j$ and, in case (b) $v_j<0$, $-v_j>0$, and the exponential is positive whether v_j is positive or

---

[2] Let us now restrict ourselves to the stable case of physical interest with all $q_j>0$.

loses more biomass than predator gains.

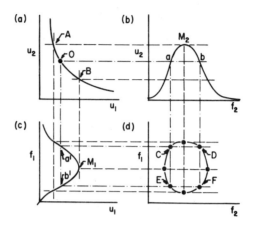

FIG. 1. Geometric scheme used to prove the periodicity of the solution (1.14) of the Volterra equations (1.1). For discussion of the scheme, see text.

negative. Hence we have $G>0$. Since $\sum \beta_j q_j$ is constant, one also finds that

$$G_0 = - \sum \beta_j q_j [1 + v_j - \exp (v_j)] = \text{const.} \quad (1.9b)$$

The constancy of G in the case of two competing species can be used to show that they vary periodically in the manner described above. Equations (1.1) are equivalent to (1.2) when $n=2$ if one sets

$$\alpha_1 = k_1, \qquad \alpha_2 = -k_2, \quad (1.10a)$$

$$\lambda_1 \beta_1 = -a_{12} = a_{21} = \lambda_2 \beta_2. \quad (1.10b)$$

Then, we have

$$q_1 = \alpha_2/\lambda_2, \qquad q_2 = \alpha_1/\lambda_1. \quad (1.11)$$

If we define

$$f_1 = N_1(t)\lambda_2/\alpha_2, \qquad f_2 = N_2(t)\lambda_1/\alpha_1, \quad (1.12)$$

and note that

$$v_j = \log f_j \quad \text{with} \quad j=1, 2, \quad (1.13)$$

10

we see that (1.9a) is equivalent to the statement that, at any time t,

$$[f_1 \exp{(-f_1)}]^{1/\alpha_1}[f_2 \exp{(-f_2)}]^{1/\alpha_2} = \text{const.} \quad (1.14)$$

The periodic character of this solution can be seen through the aid of the four diagrams in Fig. 1. If we let

$$u_1 = [f_1 \exp{(-f_1)}]^{1/\alpha_1}; \quad u_2 = [f_2 \exp{(-f_2)}]^{1/\alpha_2}, \quad (1.15)$$

then (1.14) becomes the equation of a hyperbola

$$u_1 u_2 = \text{const} \quad (1.16)$$

which is plotted in Fig. 1(a). Figures 1(b) and 1(c) show the behavior of u_1 and u_2 as functions of f_1 and f_2, respectively. An important feature of these two figures is that u_1 and u_2 attain maximum values which are identified by M_1 and M_2 in these figures. Hence the relevant region of the hyperbola in Fig. 1(a) is bounded by points A and B. Note that a typical point O between A and B corresponds to two values of f_2 (a and b) and to two values of f_1, a' and b'. Hence on Fig. 1(d) which relates f_1 and f_2, the point O corresponds to the four points C, D, E, and F. As one goes from points A to B in Fig. 1(a), one traces out the closed curve in Fig. 1(d). The end points A and B correspond, respectively, to extrema in f_2 and f_1 on Fig. 1(d).

Equations (1.1a), (1.1b), and (1.12) imply that the initial conditions (for $i = 1, 2$) $f_i(0) = 0$ and $f_i(0) = 1$ yield species populations which will remain at their initial values forever. While the first set of conditions is of no interest, the second represents a true equilibrium state. Any other set of initial populations yields periodic population variations which trace a closed curve about the equilibrium point in a counterclockwise direction. There is, of course, a whole family of these curves, each member depending upon the initial conditions. Curves which lie close to the equilibrium point are essentially ellipses, whereas those which are farther away begin to look like lopsided eggs (see Fig. 2).

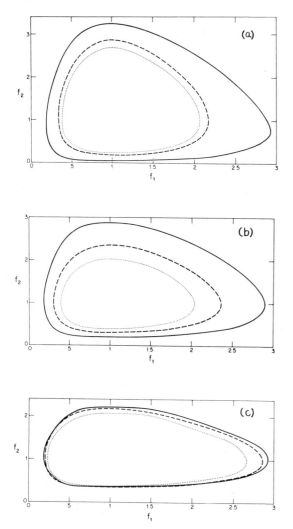

FIG. 2. Variation of f_1 with respect to f_2 for various values of the parameters and initial values $f_1(0)$ and $f_2(0)$. (a) $(\alpha_1/\alpha_2) = \frac{1}{2}$ with the values of $f_1(0)$ and $f_2(0)$: —, 0.2 and 0.8; ---, 2.0 and 0.5; $\cdots$, 0.5 and 2.0. (b) $(\alpha_1/\alpha_2) = 1$ with the values of $f_1(0)$ and $f_2(0)$: —, 0.2 and 0.8; ---, 0.5 and 2.0; $\cdots$, 1.0 and 0.8. (c) $(\alpha_1/\alpha_2) = 2$ with the values of $f_1(0)$ and $f_2(0)$: —, 0.2 and 0.8; ---, 0.2 and 2.0; $\cdots$, 2.0 and 0.5.

For each set of initial values $f_1(0)$ and $f_2(0)$, one finds a solution of (1.14) (for fixed α_1 and α_2). The points on closed curves such as those in Fig. 2 can be identified with the time by integrating

$$t = \int_{f_1(0)}^{f_1(t)} df_1 / \alpha_1 f_1 (1 - f_2). \tag{1.17}$$

Since f_2 is given as a function of f_1 on the curve in Fig. 2, one could start at the initial values $[f_1(0), f_2(0)]$, integrate numerically along the curve a short distance to a prechosen point $f_1(t)$, and, from the value of t determined from (1.17), one would identify the time appropriate for that value of $f_1(t)$. This process could be continued until a full oscillation would be completed. The time variation of the two populations are given in Fig. 3 for several sets of parameters.

It is interesting that without formally solving the dynamical equations (1.2), we can say quite a bit (especially for a two-species system) about the long time averages of various functions of N_i's.

Let us integrate our basic rate equation (1.2) from $t=0$ to T. Then, after dividing by T, we have

$$\lim_{T \to \infty} \{ T^{-1} \log N_i(T) - T^{-1} \log N_i(0) \}$$

$$= k_i \beta_i + \sum_{j=1}^{n} a_{ij} [\![N_j]\!],$$

where $[\![\ ]\!]$ denote the time averages. Our conservation condition (1.9) prevents any $v_i(T)$ from increasing indefinitely and therefore prevents $N_i(T)$ from increasing indefinitely. Hence, if $N_i(T)$ does not vanish as $T \to \infty$, the left-hand side of the above equation vanishes so that

$$k_i \beta_i + \sum_{j=1}^{n} a_{ij} [\![N_j]\!] = 0.$$

Whether $N_i(T) \to 0$ or not, we can multiply both sides of the above equation by $[\![N_i]\!]$ to obtain

$$[\![N_i]\!] (k_i \beta_i + \sum_{j=1}^{n} a_{ij} [\![N_j]\!]) = 0, \qquad i = 1, 2, \cdots, n.$$

VOLTERRA MODEL

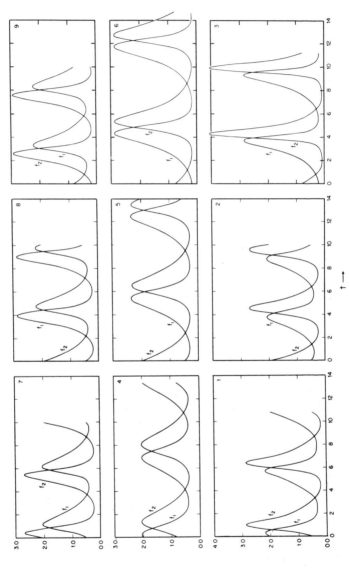

Fig. 3. Time variation of the two populations for several values of parameters. (1), (2), (3), $\alpha_1 = 1$, $\alpha_2 = 2$; (4), (5), (6), $\alpha_1 = \alpha_2 = 1$; (7), (8), (9), $\alpha_1 = 2$, $\alpha_2 = 1$. The initial values are the values for $t = 0$.

14

Hence the time averages of the populations of our n species satisfy the same equations as the equilibrium values [Eq. (1.5)] so that

$$[[N_i]] = q_i \qquad i = 1, 2, \cdots, n. \qquad (1.18)$$

Time averages of other functions of N_i are derived in Appendix A. In particular, we show that for two-species systems

$$[[N_1 N_2]] = q_1 q_2, \qquad (1.19)$$

$$\beta_1 [[y_1^2]]/q_1 = \beta_2 [[y_2^2]]/q_2 = \theta_2, \qquad (1.20)$$

where

$$y_i = N_i - q_i, \qquad i = 1, 2, \qquad (1.21)$$

and θ_2 is a constant. For $[[y_i^p]]$, the expressions similar to (1.20) exist. It is further shown that if we know $[[N_1^p]]$, we can calculate $[[N_2^p]]$ and $[[N_1^p N_2^p]]$. In addition to the time averages of polynomials of N_1 and N_2, time averages of polynomials of v_1 and v_2 and their time derivatives are also calculated. In particular, it has been shown [(A23) and (A24)] that

$$a_{12}/\beta_1 = [[\dot{v}_1 v_2]]/[[v_2 y_2]] \qquad (1.22)$$

$$= [[\dot{v}_1 y_2]]/[[y_2^2]]. \qquad (1.23)$$

These equations can be used to calculate a_{12}/β_1, one of the "rate constants" in (1.2), if the time-dependent variation of $N_1(t)$ and $N_2(t)$ is known. The latter, presumably, can be measured experimentally.

We have also derived the equations which satisfy the time averages of various functions of N_i in systems of many species. The two-species averages given above are consistent with these equations.

The fact that G as given by (1.9a) is a sum of individual terms, each relating to a separate species, is of considerable importance. It allows a natural specification of the "components" of the system in the sense usual in statistical mechanics. This was recognized by Kerner (1957), who constructed a statistical mechanics of the Volterra system. He constructed a Gibbs' ensemble of the Volterra systems such that all systems were controlled by the dynamical equation, (1.2), and such that each system represented one of the possible sets of initial values of $\{v_i\}$ consistent with the constant, G. The state of each member of the ensemble was represented by a point in the phase space $v_1 \cdots v_n$; that of the ensemble, by the collection of phase points. As the ensemble evolves in time, the collection of points moves in the phase space. If $\rho(v_1 \cdots v_n)$ denotes the density of phase points at $(v_1 \cdots v_n)$ in the phase space, the equation of continuity is

$$\partial\rho/\partial t + \sum_i \partial(\rho\dot{v}_i)/\partial v_i = 0. \qquad (1.24)$$

Since, from (1.8),

$$\partial\dot{v}_i/\partial v_i = 0, \qquad (1.25)$$

(1.24) becomes

$$D\rho/Dt \equiv (\partial\rho/\partial t) + \sum \dot{v}_i(\partial\rho/\partial v_i) = 0 \qquad (1.26)$$

which is the Liouville's theorem of the conservation of density in phase space.

If, in addition, one assumes (a) that in the ensemble we contemplate all possible copies of a system compatible with whatever information we have about it (e.g., G) and weigh each copy equally, and (b) that time averages over a single system are the same as the averages over a suitable ensemble (ergodic theorem), then one can construct a statistical mechanics of the system. This is exactly what Kerner assumed.

Suppose our knowledge about the system is limited only to the initial value of G, $G(0)$. Then we can define a microcanonical ensemble such that the ensemble average $E\{f\}$ of any function $f(v_1, \cdots, v_n)$ of phase coordinates is

$$E\{f\} = \int \rho f \, d\tau / \int \rho \, d\tau, \qquad (1.27)$$

where

$$\rho = \rho_0 \delta\{G - G(0)\}, \qquad (1.28)$$

the integrals extend over all the phase space, and ρ_0 is an unimportant normalizing factor.

Using a well known trick (Khinchin, 1959) we find

$$E\{f\} = \int_{G(0)} f \frac{ds}{|\nabla G|} \bigg/ \int_{G(0)} \frac{ds}{|\nabla G|}, \qquad (1.29)$$

where ds is an element of area on a surface of constant G, the surface integral extends over the surface $G = G_0$, and

$$\nabla G = \sum_i (\partial G/\partial v_i)\hat{v}_i, \qquad (1.30)$$

where $\hat{v}_i$ is a unit vector in the v_i direction. In Appendix B, using (1.29), we have calculated the microcanonical averages of various functions of N_i. In particular, we show that these averages are

$$E\{N_i\} = q_i, \qquad (1.31\text{a})$$

$$E\{N_i N_j\} = q_i q_j, \qquad (1.31\text{b})$$

$$E\{y_i^2\} = q_i \theta_2/\beta_i, \qquad (1.31\text{c})$$

$$E\{y_i^3\} = q_i \theta_3/\beta_i^2, \qquad (1.31\text{d})$$

where θ_2 and θ_3 are constants. Expressions similar to (1.31c) can be derived for $E\{y_i^p\}$, p an integer. In addition we show that if $E\{N_i^p\}$ is known for all i and p, $E\{N_1^{p_1} N_2^{p_2} \cdots N_n^{p_n}\}$ can be calculated. We further show that if we assert that

$$E\{N_1^{p_1} N_2^{p_2} \cdots N_n^{p_n}\} = E\{N_1^{p_1}\} E\{N_2^{p_2}\} \cdots E\{N_n^{p_n}\},$$

$$(1.32)$$

then all the microcanonical ensemble averages can be expressed in terms of q_i, β_i, and $E\{N_i^2\}$, and

$$E\{y_i^p\} = (p-1)(\theta_2/\beta_i)[E\{y_i^{p-1}\} + q_i E\{y_i^{p-2}\}]. \quad (1.33)$$

Thus all the averages of polynomials in N_i can be expressed in terms of q_i, β_i, and θ_2. In Sec. 4 we will determine the conditions under which (1.32) is true.

To study the behavior of a part, or component, consisting of, say, only ν of the total n species, Kerner (1957) assumes that the phase points corresponding to these components are distributed according to the law

$$\rho_\nu = \frac{\exp\,(-G_\nu/\Theta)}{\int \exp\,(-G_\nu/\Theta)\,d\tau_\nu} \qquad (1.34)$$

which defines the Gibbs' canonical ensemble. The canonical average $\langle f \rangle$ of any function f is

$$\langle f \rangle = \int\!\!\int f\rho_\nu\,d\tau_\nu. \qquad (1.35)$$

In (1.34), Θ is a constant characterizing the distribution. Because of the decomposibility of G, into its components, i.e.,

$$G = \sum_i G_i, \qquad \text{See} \quad l^7a$$

we have

$$\langle f_1(y_1)f_2(y_2)\cdots f_n(y_n) \rangle = \langle f_1(y_1) \rangle \langle f_2(y_2) \rangle \cdots \langle f_n(y_n) \rangle.$$
$$(1.36)$$

In Appendix C we have derived the expressions for various functions of N_i, v_i, and their time derivatives. In particular, we show that

$$\langle y_i \rangle = 0, \qquad \text{i.e.,} \quad \langle N_i \rangle = q_i, \qquad (1.37)$$

equal to the time average and the microcanonical average. Furthermore, we have

$$\langle y_i^2 \rangle = \Theta q_i/\beta_i$$
$$= q_i\langle y_i v_i \rangle, \qquad (1.38)$$
$$\langle y_i^p \rangle = (\Theta/\beta_i)\,(p-1)[\langle y_i^{p-1} \rangle + q_i\langle y_i^{p-2} \rangle]. \quad (1.39)$$

Equation (1.38) is exactly the same as for the microcanonical ensemble if we identify Θ with θ_2 [Eq. (1.31c)] of the microcanonical ensemble. All other averages are also the same, provided we assume (1.36) to be true also for the microcanonical ensemble. This can be true for the microcanonical ensemble, but need not be. The validity of (1.36) enables us to describe all the averages in terms of a single parameter Θ. If it is not valid, we need a number of parameters, one for each of the averages of N_i^2, N_i^3, $\cdots$. Thus it is important for us to test the validity of the canonical ensemble, i.e., whether canonical ensemble averages are the same as the corresponding time averages, i.e., whether the ergodic theorem is true for canonical ensemble averages. This will be investigated in Sec. 4.

It should be noted that there exists a constant of motion only because of the special form of the Volterra equation (1.2). If one adds other terms in (1.2) to include other aspects of the population, in general there will not be any constant of motion. For example, one aspect which is neglected in the Volterra model (although it was well known to him) is the approach to saturation of a population which must survive on limited resources. If a species is not preyed upon by other species, it is expected that its population will saturate and not continue to grow indefinitely. This point was first made by the Belgian mathematician, Verhulst (1845), when he was asked if the population of Belgium would grow exponentially in the manner proposed by Malthus. The Verhulst population growth equation (which was rediscovered by Pearl and Reed, 1920) is

$$dN/dt = kN(\theta - N)/\theta, \qquad (1.40)$$

θ being the saturation level. If such a term is introduced into (1.2), the resulting set of equations is

$$\frac{dN_j}{dt} = k_j N_j \frac{\theta_j - \frac{1}{2}[1 + \text{sgn } k_j]N_j}{\theta_j} + \beta_j^{-1} N_j \sum_1^n a_{ji} N_i. \qquad (1.41)$$

The influence of such saturation terms is to damp out fluctuations in the population of species j. However, the time scale may be so long for that damping effect that an enormous number of oscillations may occur during the damping relaxation time. In Sec. 3 we will retain this term only when it is necessary to keep a population from exploding.

In the steady state, the populations of the various species $\{q_j\}$ are given by

$$k_j \beta_j \frac{\theta_j - \frac{1}{2}[1 + \text{sgn } k_j]q_j}{\theta_j} + \sum_1^n a_{ji} q_i = 0. \qquad (1.42)$$

19

Hence, in terms of v_j, we have

$$\beta_j \dot{v}_j = -\tfrac{1}{2} k_j [1 + \text{sgn } k_j](q_j/\theta_j)$$
$$\times [\exp (v_j) - 1]\beta_j + \sum_i a_{ji} q_i [\exp (v_i) - 1]. \quad (1.43)$$

If we follow the ideas used in the derivation of (1.9), we find that

$$dG/dt = -\tfrac{1}{2} \sum_j \beta_j k_j (1 + \text{sgn } k_j)(q_j^2/\theta_j)[\exp (v_j) - 1]^2 < 0$$

$$(1.44)$$

with

$$\tfrac{1}{2} k_j \{1 + \text{sgn } k_j\} = 0 \quad \text{if} \quad k_j < 0$$
$$= k_j \quad \text{if} \quad k_j > 0.$$

The quantity G is no longer a constant of the motion when the Verhulst term is included. Instead it continually decreases in time until each N_j with $k_j > 0$ (with nonvanishing Verhulst term) approaches q_j, and then, since $v_j = \log N_j/q_j = 0$, $dG/dt \to 0$. Hence we conclude that N_j, for all those species with $k_j > 0$, approaches q_j asymptotically, and for those species with $k_j < 0$, N_j is bounded.

When one or more of the q_j's has the nonphysical characteristic of being negative, the definition (1.7) of v_j is no longer appropriate. Instead, we define v_j' by

$$N_j = q_j s_j \exp (v_j'), \quad (1.45a)$$

where

$$s_j = 1 \quad \text{if} \quad q_j > 0$$
$$= -1 \quad \text{if} \quad q_j < 0 \quad (1.45b)$$

and

$$G' = \sum q_j s_j \beta_j [\exp (v_j') - s_j v_j'] = \sum G_j'. \quad (1.46)$$

After some algebraic manipulation, we find that

$$dG'/dt = -\tfrac{1}{2} \sum \beta_j k_j (1 + \text{sgn } k_j)(q_j^2/\theta_j)$$
$$\times [\exp (v_j') - s_j]^2 < 0 \quad (1.47)$$

If the Verhulst term is absent for all the species, we have $dG'/dt = 0$, i.e., G' is a constant of motion. With this new definition (1.45a) of G, it can be shown (see Sec. 3) that if one or more q_j's are negative, at least one of the species with q_j negative will eventually vanish.

III. A Primitive Statistical Model of Population Growth

Most of this paper is concerned with statistical aspects of the population growth of individual species and of the correlations between population variation of different species. We start our presentation of this topic with a simple stochastic model.

Consider the Verhulst equation for the population growth of a single species with saturation level θ,

$$dN/dt = kN(\theta - N)/\theta. \qquad (2.1a)$$

The solution of this equation is

$$f(t) = f(0)/\{f(0) + [1 - f(0)] \exp(-kt)\} \qquad (2.1b)$$

with

$$f(t) \equiv N(t)/\theta. \qquad (2.1c)$$

It is well known that the time variation of the population of many countries can be fitted quite well by Eq. (2.1) [see, for example, Pearl (1924) and Montroll (1968)]. An excellent guide to the literature of population growth and its theory has been given by Glass (1967). The Malthusian exponentiation of population growth is just the $\theta \rightarrow \infty$ limit of (2.1a):

$$dN/dt = kN \quad \text{or} \quad N(t) = N(0) \exp(kt). \qquad (2.1d)$$

There are differential equations besides (2.1a) which lead to population saturation. One is the equation of Gompertz (1825)

$$dN/dt = -kN \log N/\theta, \qquad 0 < N \le \theta, \qquad (2.2a)$$

which was invented for the investigation of mortality rates rather than population growth. It was, however, used for fitting growth statistics. Equation (2.2a) implies that

$$\log \log [N(t)/\theta] - \log \log [N(0)/\theta] = -kt$$

and, therefore, that

$$N(t) = \theta \exp \{e^{-kt}[\log N(0)/\theta]\} \qquad (2.2b)$$

which approaches the saturation level θ as $t \to \infty$. The Gompertz form apparently became unfashionable because of computational difficulties, in precomputer days, in using the method of least squares to fit observational data (Davis, 1941).

Generally one might consider arbitrary saturation inducing functions $G(N/\theta)$ with the property

$$G(x) \to 0 \qquad \text{as } x \to 1$$

and which lead to the differential equation

$$dN/dt = kNG(N/\theta). \qquad (2.3)$$

Often $G(x) \to 1$ as $x \to 0$ as in the Verhulst case in which $G(x) = 1 - x$.

Now let us suppose that our species of interest is not only influenced by other specific species of the set of n, but also by species, say bacteria, (if the n species are larger animals) and other parasites, plant life which varies in intensity from season to season, and unspecified migrating species, etc., which affect the population of our n species in a random way. Then our basic equations for population growth might be considered to be of the form

$$\frac{dN_j}{dt} = k_j N_j G\left(\frac{N_j}{\theta_j}\right) + N_j\{U_j(t) + \beta_j^{-1} \sum_{i=1}^{n} a_{ji} N_i\}, \quad (2.4)$$

where $G(x)$ is a saturation-inducing term and $U_j(t)$ represents random unspecified influences. When the number of specified related species, n, is large and each species interacts with a fairly large number of others, one would expect a_{jk}'s of both signs to appear in (2.4) for most j. Since the population of each of the species $N_1, N_2, \cdots$ varies with the time when each is influenced by random unspecified species, the sum in (2.4) might

24

also be considered to be a random function of time. The combination of $U_j(t)$ and the sum might then be considered as a random function of time, $F_j(t)$. This consideration would lead to the species being coupled in only a random way. Since only terms with index j will appear in the resulting equation, we suppress the j in the following, and develop the consequences of postulating $F_j(t)$ to be a random function. Then (2.4) becomes

$$dN/dt = kNG(N/\theta) + NF(t). \qquad (2.5)$$

We also assume that the average value of $F(t)$ vanishes, i.e.,

$$\langle F(t) \rangle = 0. \qquad (2.6)$$

As is shown at the end of this section, nothing is basically changed when this is not so. The Fokker–Planck equation for this process follows from the standard hypothesis made in the theory of Brownian motion and random processes that

$$\langle F(t_1)F(t_2) \rangle = \sigma^2 \delta(t_1 - t_2). \qquad (2.7)$$

It may be noted that (2.5) also represents the growth of a species (in the absence of other species) in a random environment, or equivalently the growth when growth coefficient is $\bar{k} + F(t)$, where $\bar{k}$ is the average growth coefficient.

Instead of investigating the Fokker–Planck equation for the variable N, we will investigate that for the variable V defined by

$$V = \log N/\theta, \qquad (2.8)$$

this being more physically meaningful. Thus our basic equation for deriving the Fokker–Planck equation is

$$dV/dt = kG(\exp(V)) + F(t). \qquad (2.9)$$

In a short time Δt, the variation in V is

$$\Delta V = kG(\exp(V))\Delta t + \int_t^{t+\Delta t} F(t_1) \, dt_1 + O(\Delta t)^2. \quad (2.10)$$

Then, if (2.6) is valid, we find

$$A \equiv \lim_{\Delta t \to 0} \langle \Delta V \rangle / \Delta t = kG(\exp(V)), \qquad (2.11)$$

while

$$\langle (\Delta V)^2 \rangle = k^2 [G(\exp(V))]^2 (\Delta t)^2$$
$$+ \int_t^{t+\Delta t} \int_t^{t+\Delta t} \langle F(t_1) F(t_2) \rangle dt_1 \, dt_2 + O(\Delta t)^2. \quad (2.12)$$

If the classical Brownian motion postulate (2.7) is made, then

$$B \equiv \lim_{\Delta t \to 0} \langle (\Delta V)^2 \rangle / \Delta t = \sigma^2. \qquad (2.13)$$

If one assumes that $F(t)$ is generated by a Gaussian random process, the standard form for the Fokker–Planck equation for the probability that $V(t)$ has a value V at time t is (Wang and Uhlenbeck, 1930)

$$\partial P / \partial t = - (\partial / \partial V) \{ AP \} + \tfrac{1}{2} (\partial^2 / \partial V^2) \{ BP \}. \quad (2.14)$$

When A is given by (2.11), this becomes

$$\partial P / \partial t = -k(\partial / \partial V) \{ PG(\exp(V)) \} + \tfrac{1}{2} \sigma^2 (\partial^2 P / \partial V^2).$$

$$(2.15)$$

It may be noted that the Fokker–Planck equation for the variable N derived by using (2.5) when transformed into the variable V is different from (2.15).

The steady state distribution function for this case is obtained by setting $\partial P / \partial t = 0$ and letting

$$U = k \int_0^V G(\exp(V)) \, dV \text{ with } dU/dV = kG(\exp(V)).$$

$$(2.16)$$

Then (2.15) becomes

$$(\partial / \partial V) \{ -P(\partial U / \partial V) + \tfrac{1}{2} \sigma^2 (\partial P / \partial V) \} = 0 \quad (2.17)$$

from which we see that

$$(\partial / \partial V) \{ \exp(2V/\sigma^2)(\partial / \partial V) [P \exp(-2V/\sigma^2)] \} = 0.$$

$$(2.18)$$

The solution of this equation is, with P_0 being a normalizing constant,

$$P = P_0 \exp(2U/\sigma^2)$$

$$= P_0 \exp\left[2\sigma^{-2} \int_0^V G(\exp(V)) \, dV\right]. \quad (2.19)$$

In the Gompertz and Verhulst cases, this distribution becomes, respectively,

Gompertz: $P = P_0 \exp(-kV^2/\sigma^2),$ \hfill $(2.19')$

Verhulst: $P = P_0 \exp\{2k[V - \exp(V)]/\sigma^2\}.$

$$(2.19'')$$

Equation $(2.19'')$ was first derived by Leigh (1969). Leigh also derived the special form of the Fokker–Planck equation (2.15) which is appropriate for the Verhulst case.

The normalization constants are easily obtained for the two special cases $(2.19')$ and $(2.19'')$. The distribution functions in terms of the population variable are

Gompertz: $P(N, \infty) = (k/2\pi\sigma^2)^{1/2} N^{-1}$

$$\times \exp\{-k(\log[N/\theta])^2/2\sigma^2\}, \quad (2.20a)$$

Verhulst: $P(N, \infty) = [\theta\Gamma(2k\sigma^{-2})]^{-1}$

$$\times (2kN/\theta\sigma^2)^{2k/\sigma^2} \exp(-2Nk/\theta\sigma^2), \quad (2.20b)$$

where $\Gamma(x)$ is the classical gamma function.

An alternative form of the Fokker–Planck equation of our process, (2.15), is obtained by letting

$$P(V, t) = \Psi(V, t) \exp\left[k\sigma^{-2} \int_0^V G(\exp(V)) \, dV\right].$$

$$(2.21)$$

Then we find

$$(2/k)\Psi_t = \sigma^2 k^{-1} \Psi_{VV}$$
$$- \{[\partial G(\exp(V))/\partial V] + k\sigma^{-2}[G(\exp(V))]^2\}\Psi.$$

$$(2.22)$$

This is to be compared with the Schrödinger equation

$$\hbar i \Psi_t = (\hbar^2/2m)\Psi_{xx} - U(x)\Psi \qquad (2.23a)$$

and the Bloch equation in which $-it/\hbar$ is replaced by $\beta = 1/kT$ (which is used in statistical mechanics):

$$\Psi_\beta = (\hbar^2/2m)\Psi_{xx} - U(x)\Psi. \qquad (2.23b)$$

If, in the Bloch equation, we choose the mass to be $\frac{1}{2}$ and identify β with $\frac{1}{2}kt$, $\hbar^2$ with σ^2/k, and $U(x)$ with

$$W(V) \equiv k\sigma^{-2}[G(\exp(V))]^2 + \partial G(\exp(V))/\partial V,$$

$$(2.23c)$$

it has the same form as our basic equation (2.22). Of course, there is no connection between the physical significance of the two equations. However, there is a mathematical convenience in their similarity because the literature on the Schrödinger and Bloch equations is immediately available for our problem.

We begin our investigation of the statistical development of an initial population distribution by considering the Gompertz case $G(x) = -\log x$, or $G(\exp(V)) = -V$. Then (2.22) becomes

$$(2/k)\Psi_t = \sigma^2 k^{-1}\Psi_{VV} - \{-1 + k\sigma^{-2}V^2\}\Psi \quad (2.24)$$

which is essentially the Bloch equation for a harmonic oscillator. Let

$$\Psi(V, t) = \psi(V) \exp\{-\tfrac{1}{2}(\lambda-1)kt\} \qquad (2.25)$$

and

$$Vk^{1/2}\sigma^{-1} = \xi. \qquad (2.26)$$

Then $\psi(V)$, in terms of ξ, is an eigenfunction of Hermite's equation which is familiar in the theory of the harmonic oscillator:

$$d^2\psi/d\xi^2 + (\lambda - \xi^2)\psi = 0. \qquad (2.27)$$

Since our probability distribution $P(V, t)$ must vanish as $V \to \pm\infty$, this is also a property of $\psi(V)$. The appropriate characteristic values and normalized characteristic functions of (2.27) are (Titchmarsh, 1937)

$$\lambda_n = 2n+1, \qquad (2.28a)$$

$$\psi_n(\xi) = H_n(\xi) \exp\left(-\tfrac{1}{2}\xi^2\right) / [2^n n! \pi^{1/2}]^{1/2}, \quad (2.28b)$$

the $H_n(\xi)$ being the Hermite polynomials defined by

$$H_n(\xi) = (-1)^n (d/d\xi)^n \exp\left(-\xi^2\right), \qquad (2.28c)$$

so that

$$H_0 = 1, \qquad H_1 = 2\xi; \qquad H_2 = 4\xi^2, \qquad H_3 = 8\xi^3 - 12\xi; \text{ etc.}$$

$$(2.28d)$$

The solution of (2.27) is a linear combination of the ψ_n's:

$$\Psi(V, t) = \sum_{n=0}^{\infty} c_n \psi_n(\xi) \exp\left(-nkt\right), \qquad (2.29)$$

where the c_n's are to be obtained from the initial ($t=0$) distribution function $P(V, 0)$ by employing the orthogonality of the ψ_n's. When $t=0$, $\Psi(V, 0)$ can be expressed in terms of $P(V, 0)$ using (2.21) and (2.26):

$$\Psi(V, 0) = P(V, 0) \exp\left(kV^2/2\sigma^2\right)$$

$$= P(V, 0) \exp\left(\tfrac{1}{2}\xi^2\right). \qquad (2.30a)$$

Hence, we have

$$c_n = \int_{-\infty}^{\infty} \psi_n(\xi) P(V, 0) \exp\left(\tfrac{1}{2}\xi^2\right) d\xi \quad (2.30b)$$

and, in particular,

$$c_0 = \pi^{-1/4} \int_{-\infty}^{\infty} P(V, 0) k^{1/2} \sigma^{-1} \, dV = k^{1/2}/\sigma\pi^{1/4} \qquad (2.31)$$

since $P(V, 0)$ must be normalized to unity. Then, combining (2.21), (2.29), and (2.31) gives

$$P(V, t) = (k/\pi\sigma^2)^{1/2} \exp\left(-kV^2/\sigma^2\right)$$

$$+ \sum_{n=1}^{\infty} c_n \psi_n(\xi) \exp\left(-nkt - kV^2\sigma^{-2}\right). \quad (2.32)$$

29

The c_n's for $n \geq 1$ depend on the initial conditions while the first (time-independent term), which gives the equilibrium distribution, is independent of the initial distribution and is in agreement with (2.19′).

There is an alternative form for $P(V, t)$ which contains $P(V, 0)$ explicitly, instead of the c_n's. First suppose that

$$P(V, 0) = \delta(V - V_0) \quad \text{with} \quad \xi_0 \equiv V_0 k^{1/2}/\sigma. \quad (2.33)$$

Then, from (2.30b) and (2.26), we have

$$c_n = (k^{1/2}/\sigma)\psi_n(\xi_0) \exp (V_0^2 k/2\sigma^2) \quad (2.34)$$

and, from (2.32),

$$P(V, V_0; t) = \frac{k^{1/2}}{\sigma} \exp \left(\frac{(V_0^2 - V^2)k}{2\sigma^2} \right)$$

$$\times \sum_{n=0}^{\infty} \psi_n(\xi)\psi_n(\xi_0)[\exp (-kt)]^n. \quad (2.35)$$

Using Mehler's formula for the sum (Titchmarsh 1937),

$$\sum_{n=0}^{\infty} \psi_n(\xi)\psi_n(\xi_0)\alpha^n$$

$$= [\pi(1-\alpha^2)]^{-1/2} \exp \left(\frac{\xi^2 - \xi_0^2}{2} - \frac{(\xi - \xi_0\alpha)^2}{1-\alpha^2} \right), \quad (2.36)$$

we find that an initial delta function distribution develops according to

$$P(V, V_0; t) = \left(\frac{k}{\pi\sigma^2[1 - \exp (-2kt)]} \right)^{1/2}$$

$$\times \exp - \left(\frac{[V - V_0 \exp (-kt)]^2 k}{\sigma^2[1 - \exp (-2kt)]} \right). \quad (2.37)$$

An arbitrary initial distribution develops according to

$$P(V, t) = \int_{-\infty}^{\infty} P(V, V_0; t)P(V_0, 0) \, dV_0. \quad (2.38)$$

The first few moments of (N/θ) are easily found from the distribution function (2.37) when N is known to have the value N_0 when $t=0$. The calculation of

$$\langle (N/\theta)^{2\lambda} \rangle = \langle \exp(2\lambda V) \rangle \qquad (2.39)$$

using (2.37) as the weight function leads to easily carried out Gaussian integrals. One finds that

$$\langle (N/\theta)^{2\lambda} \rangle = \exp\left(\lambda \{ 2V_0 \exp(-kt) \right.$$
$$\left. + \lambda(\sigma^2/k)[1- \exp(-2kt)] \} \right) \quad (2.40)$$

which implies that

$$\langle N/\theta \rangle = \exp\{ V_0 \exp(-kt) + (\sigma^2/4k)[1- \exp(-2kt)] \}$$
$$= (N_0/\theta)^{(\exp-kt)} \exp\{ (\sigma^2/4k)[1- \exp(-2kt)] \},$$
$$(2.41)$$

while

$$\langle (N-\bar{N})^2 \rangle / (\bar{N})^2$$
$$= -1 + \exp\{ (\sigma^2/2k)[1- \exp(-2kt)] \}. \quad (2.42)$$

The next special case which we consider is the Verhulst case with

$$G(x) = 1 - x. \qquad (2.43)$$

The basic equations (2.21) and (2.22) then become

$$P(V, t) = \Psi(V, t) \exp\{ -k\sigma^{-2}[1+V- \exp(V)] \}$$
$$(2.44a)$$

and

$$(2/k)\Psi_t = \sigma^2 k^{-1}\Psi_{VV}$$
$$- \{ - \exp(V) + k\sigma^{-2}[1- \exp(V)]^2 \}\Psi. \quad (2.44b)$$

With a few trivial definitions, we can put this equation into the same form as the Bloch equation for a diatomic molecule whose atoms interact according to the Morse potential.

31

We note from (2.23c) and (2.44b) that

$$W(V) = k\sigma^{-2}[1 - \exp(V)]^2 - \exp(V)$$
$$= A[\exp(2x) - 2\exp(x)] + k\sigma^{-2}, \quad (2.45)$$

where

$$x \equiv V - V^*, \qquad \exp(V^*) \equiv 1 + (\sigma^2/2k), \quad (2.46)$$

$$A = k\sigma^{-2}(1 + \tfrac{1}{2}\sigma^2 k^{-1})^2. \quad (2.47)$$

If we introduce a new function Φ by

$$\Psi(V, t) = \Phi \exp\{-\tfrac{1}{2}k(k\sigma^{-2} + E)t\} \quad (2.48)$$

then the equation for Φ is

$$(\sigma^2/k)\Phi_{xx} + \{E - A[\exp(2x) - 2\exp(x)]\}\Phi = 0 \quad (2.49)$$

which is just the Schrödinger equation for a diatomic molecule with a Morse potential when the reduced mass is taken to be $\tfrac{1}{2}$, and $\hbar^2$ is again identified with σ^2/k. Generally our x is replaced by $-x$ in studying diatomic molecules. Mathematically this difference is of no importance. We seek solutions of (2.49) such that $\phi(x) \to 0$ as $x \to \pm\infty$.

Let us examine several regimes in the population growth process. First consider the Malthusian regime for which $\theta \to \infty$. When $G(x) \to 1$ as $x \to 0$, which is the case for the Verhulst but not for the Gompertz model, the basic equation (2.15) becomes

$$P_t = -kP_V + \tfrac{1}{2}\sigma^2 P_{VV} \quad (2.50)$$

in the Malthusian limit independent of the detailed form of $G(x)$, provided that $G(0) = 1$. This equation is easily solved by using Fourier transforms. Define $p(t, \lambda)$ by

$$P(t, V) = (2\pi)^{-1/2} \int_{-\infty}^{\infty} \exp(i\lambda V)p(t, \lambda)\, d\lambda, \quad (2.51a)$$

$$p(t, \lambda) = (2\pi)^{-1/2} \int_{-\infty}^{\infty} \exp(-i\lambda V)P(t, V)\, dV. \quad (2.51b)$$

Then, we find

$$dp/dt + (ik\lambda + \tfrac{1}{2}\sigma^2\lambda^2)p = 0 \qquad (2.52)$$

and

$$p(t, \lambda) = p(0, \lambda)\exp[-(ik\lambda + \tfrac{1}{2}\sigma^2\lambda^2)t] \qquad (2.53)$$

so that, from (2.51),

$$P(t, V) = (2\pi)^{-1} \int_{-\infty}^{\infty} \int_{-\infty}^{\infty} P(0, V')$$

$$\times \exp[-i\lambda(kt - V + V') - \tfrac{1}{2}\sigma^2\lambda^2 t]d\lambda\, dV'$$

$$= (2t\pi\sigma^2)^{-1/2} \int_{-\infty}^{\infty} P(0, V')$$

$$\times \exp[-(V - V' - kt)^2/2t\sigma^2]\, dV'. \qquad (2.54)$$

In the case in which the population is precisely N_0 at time $t=0$, we have

$$P(0, V') = \delta(V' - V_0), \qquad (2.55a)$$

where

$$V' - V_0 = \log(N'/N_0), \qquad (2.55b)$$

$$N'/N_0 = \exp(V' - V_0). \qquad (2.55c)$$

The probability that V lies between V and $V + dV$ is

$$P(t, V)dV = \frac{\exp[-(V - V_0 - kt)^2/2t\sigma^2]dV}{(2t\pi\sigma^2)^{1/2}},$$

$$-\infty < V < \infty, \qquad (2.56)$$

so that, as $\sigma \to 0$, V follows the Malthusian exponential trajectory

$$V - V_0 = kt \quad \text{or} \quad N/N_0 = \exp(kt). \qquad (2.57)$$

The probability that N lies between N and $N + dN$ at time t, generally, is

$$P(t, N)dN$$

$$= \frac{dN\exp\{-(\log[(N/N_0)\exp(-kt)])^2/2t\sigma^2\}}{N(2t\pi\sigma^2)^{1/2}},$$

$$0 \leq N < \infty. \qquad (2.58)$$

The first two moments of this distribution are

$$\bar{N} = N_0 \exp\,(k + \tfrac{1}{2}\sigma^2)t, \quad (2.59a)$$

$$\langle (N - \bar{N})^2 \rangle / \bar{N}^2 = -1 + \exp\,(t\sigma^2). \quad (2.59b)$$

The next regime we consider is that in which V is small. This corresponds to a population which deviates only slightly from saturation, i.e., $N/\theta \simeq 1$ so that

$$V = \log\,(N/\theta) = \log\,[1 + (N/\theta - 1)] \simeq (N/\theta) - 1 \simeq 0.$$
$$(2.60)$$

At the same time that we let $V \to 0$, we work in the regime

$$k/\sigma^2 \to \infty \quad \text{or} \quad \sigma^2/k \to 0$$

so that

$$\eta = V k^{1/2}/\sigma \quad (2.61)$$

is finite. Under these conditions, since we are restricting ourselves to examples for which $G(1) = 0$, we find

$$G(\exp\,(V)) = G(1 + [\exp\,(V) - 1]) = VG'(1) + O(V^2),$$
$$(2.62a)$$

$$2k\sigma^{-2} \int_0^V G(\exp\,(V))\,dV$$
$$= k\sigma^{-2}V^2G(1) + k\sigma^{-2}O(V^3) \to -\alpha\eta^2. \quad (2.62b)$$

We have defined the parameter α as

$$\alpha = -G'(1). \quad (2.63)$$

On this basis, the equilibrium distribution function of V is (see 2.19)

$$P(V) = (\alpha k/\pi\sigma^2)^{1/2} \exp\,(-\alpha k V^2/\sigma^2). \quad (2.64)$$

The function $W(V)$ defined by (2.23c) and which appears in our basic rate equation (2.24), is found in the regime of interest from (2.62a) and

$$dG(\exp\,(V))/dV = \exp\,(V)G'(1)$$
$$+ 2[\exp\,(V) - 1]\exp\,(V)G''(1) + \cdots. \quad (2.65a)$$

As $V \to 0$, we have

$$dG(\exp (V))/dV \to G'(1), \qquad (2.65b)$$

while

$$k\sigma^{-2}[G(\exp (V))]^2 = k\sigma^{-2}V^2[G'(1)]^2$$
$$+ k\sigma^{-2}O(V^3) \to \alpha^2\eta^2. \quad (2.66)$$

Hence in our regime

$$W(V) = -\alpha + \eta^2\alpha^2. \qquad (2.67)$$

In the Verhulst case with $G(x) = 1-x$, we have $\alpha = 1$. Other saturation inducing functions $G(x)$ lead to other values of α. From (2.22), (2.23c), and (2.67) we find

$$(2/k)\Psi_t = \Psi_{\eta\eta} + (\alpha - \alpha^2\eta^2)\Psi. \qquad (2.68)$$

Now let

$$\Psi(\eta, t) = \phi(\eta) \exp\left[-\tfrac{1}{2}k(E-\alpha)t\right], \qquad (2.69a)$$

then we have

$$\phi_{\eta\eta} + (E - \alpha^2\eta^2)\phi = 0 \qquad (2.69b)$$

or

$$\phi_{\xi\xi} + (\lambda - \xi^2)\phi = 0 \qquad (2.69c)$$

if we define

$$\lambda = E/\alpha \quad \text{and} \quad \xi = \eta\alpha^{1/2}.$$

Equations (2.69a)–(2.69c) are essentially the same as those obtained for the Gompertz model (2.25)–(2.27). The ideas presented for the investigation of that case are immediately applicable here. One finds that if initially the population is N_0 so that $V_0 = \log N_0/\theta$, then

$$P(V, V_0; t) = (\alpha k/\pi\sigma^2[1 - \exp (-2\alpha kt)])^{1/2}$$

$$\times \exp -\{[V - V_0 \exp (-\alpha kt)]^2 k\alpha/\sigma^2$$

$$\times [1 - \exp (2\alpha kt)]\}. \quad (2.70)$$

If the initial distribution of population is $P(V_0, t)$, then again we have

$$P(V, t) = \int_{-\infty}^{\infty} P(V, V_0; t) P(V_0, 0) \, dV_0.$$

We can summarize our results for the two regimes:

(a) $\theta \to \infty$,
(b) $V \to 0$ and $\sigma^2/k \to 0$ such that $(V\sigma k^{-1/2}) = $ const,

by stating that, as long as $G(0) = 1$ (as is the case for the Verhulst model), (i) the population distribution develops according to (2.58) in the Malthus range (a), and (ii) that when the population is near saturation, it fluctuates according to the distribution function (2.70) independent of the details of the model. The only parameter which distinguishes one model from another is

$$\alpha = -G'(1)$$

which has the value 1 for the Verhulst distribution.

The population distribution in other regimes besides (a) and (b) depends on the detailed behavior of $G(x)$. We now consider the Verhulst model over all regimes by returning to Eq. (2.49), which is the Schrödinger equation for the Morse potential if one identifies $\hbar^2$ with σ^2/k.

The energy levels of a Morse oscillator are known to be

$$E_n = -A\{1 - (\hbar^2/A)^{1/2}(n + \tfrac{1}{2})\}^2. \qquad (2.71a)$$

In terms of our parameters (which are related to $\hbar$ and A by (2.23c) and (2.47), it is easy to show that

$$\tfrac{1}{2}k(E + k\sigma^{-2}) = nk(1 - n\sigma^2 k^{-1}), \quad n = 0, 1, 2, \cdots, [k/\sigma^2],$$

$$(2.71b)$$

where $[x]$ is the integral part of the number x, i.e., the largest integer less than or equal to x.

The general solution of (2.44b) is then

$$\Psi(V, t) = \sum_{n=0}^{[k\sigma^{-2}]} c_n \phi_n(x) \exp\left[-nk(t-n\sigma^2 k^{-1})\right]$$

$$+ \text{ continuous spectra contribution,} \quad (2.72a)$$

where the function $\phi_n(x)$ is the nth of the orthonormal wave functions of (2.49). The constants c_n must be determined from the initial distribution $P(V, 0)$ which is related to $\Psi(V, 0)$ by (2.44a).

An alternative form for our basic equation (2.49) is

$$\Phi_{xx} + k\sigma^{-2}\{(E+A) - A[\exp(x)-1]^2\}\Phi = 0 \quad (2.72b)$$

whose normalized solutions are (Trischka and Salwen, 1959)

$$\phi_n(x) = M_n z^{1/2(q-2n-1)} \exp(-z/2) F_n(z) \quad (2.73a)$$

in the regime of the discrete spectrum. Here we have

$$z = q \exp(V-V_0) \quad \text{with} \quad q = 2k\sigma^{-2}[1+(\sigma^2/2k)],$$

$$(2.73b)$$

$$\tfrac{1}{2}(q-2n-1) = k\sigma^{-2} - n, \quad (2.73c)$$

$$F_n(z) = \sum_{i=1}^{n} \binom{n}{i} \frac{(-z)^i}{(q-2n)_i}, \quad \binom{n}{i} = \frac{n!}{i!(n-i)!}, \quad (2.73d)$$

$$M_n^2 = \frac{1}{n!} \frac{(q-2n)_n}{\Gamma(q-2n-1)}, \quad (2.73e)$$

the definition of $(a)_n$ being

$$(a)_n = 1 \qquad\qquad\qquad \text{if} \quad n=0$$

$$= a(a+1)\cdots(a+n-1) \quad \text{if} \quad n>1. \quad (2.73f)$$

In particular, we find

$$F_0(z) = 1, \qquad M_0^2 = \{\Gamma(2k\sigma^{-2})\}^{-1}, \quad (2.74a)$$

$$\phi_0(x) = \{\Gamma(2k\sigma^{-2})\}^{-1/2}(2k\sigma^{-2})^{k\sigma^{-2}}$$

$$\times \exp\{-k\sigma^{-2}[\exp(V)-V]\}. \quad (2.74b)$$

37

Since the $\Psi_n(x)$'s form an orthonormal set, the constants c_n in (2.72a) have the form

$$c_n = \int_{-\infty}^{\infty} \phi_n(x) P(V, 0) \exp\left(-\frac{k[V - \exp\ (V)]}{\sigma^2}\right) dV,$$

(2.75a)

where, in particular, since $P(V, 0)$ is normalized to unity,

$$c_0 = (2k/\sigma^2)^{k/\sigma^2} \{\Gamma(2k\sigma^{-2})\}^{-1/2}.$$

(2.75b)

Hence the final form for our required distribution function $P(V, 0)$ is

$$P(V, t) = \frac{(2k\sigma^{-2})^{k/\sigma^2}}{\Gamma(2k\sigma^{-2})} \exp\ \{-2k\sigma^{-2}[\exp\ (V) - V]\}$$

$$+ \sum_{n=1}^{[k/\sigma^2]} c_n \phi_n(x)$$

$$\times \exp\ \{k[V - \exp\ (V)]\sigma^{-2} - nkt(1 - n\sigma^2 k^{-1})\}$$

$+$ contribution of the continuous spectrum.   (2.76)

The continuous spectrum contribution is of the form

$$\int_0^{\infty} F(E, x)\ \exp\left[\frac{\frac{1}{2}k[V - \exp\ (V)]}{\sigma^2}\right]$$

$$\times \exp\ (-\tfrac{1}{2}kt[E + k\sigma^{-2}])\ dE,$$

where the function F depends on confluent hypergeometric functions. We will discuss this in detail elsewhere. The important characteristic of this expression is that it decays very rapidly with t so that one does not have to be very far out of the Malthus range before it is negligible. In the contribution of the discrete spectrum, E_n is negative so that it subtracts from $k\sigma^{-2}$, while in the continuous range it is positive so that it enhances $k\sigma^{-2}$. As $t \to \infty$ (2.76) reduces to the equilibrium formula (2.19b).

The above ideas can be summarized by dividing the population growth process into three regimes. In the first (the $\theta \to \infty$ regime), the population grows freely with no interference. This is analogous to a free particle which accelerates in a field. In the second regime, the population has grown to the point where it is affected by other influences such as other species (and, in the case of human population growth, by fluctuations in the economy, by changes in personal attitudes, by agricultural successes and failures, etc.). In our Morse type equation, this is analogous to the system falling into the highest energy bound state of the Morse potential, then dropping into lower energy states until it reaches the ground state. In the ground state, the population fluctuates around its average value with statistics characterized by the equilibrium distribution (2.19b). These fluctuations are the analogs of the zero point fluctuations of a Morse oscillator.

We close this section with a remark about the hypothesis (2.6) that $\langle F(t) \rangle = 0$. Suppose that this is not the case and that $\langle F(t) \rangle = a$. Then we can let

$$F(t) = a + \delta F, \tag{2.77a}$$

where $\langle \delta F \rangle = 0$. On this basis, (2.5) becomes

$$dN/dt = aN + kNG(N/\theta) + N\delta F. \tag{2.77b}$$

The parameters k and θ can usually be changed to put this equation into the same form that it would have had if $\langle F \rangle = 0$. In the Gompertz case, we can write

$$dN/dt = kN \log (N/\theta') + N\delta F, \tag{2.78a}$$

where θ' is now defined to be

$$\theta' = \theta \exp (a/k). \tag{2.78b}$$

If one generalizes the Verhulst saturation inducing function to

$$G(x) = 1 - x^\nu \tag{2.79a}$$

($\nu = 1$ corresponds to Verhulst case), then (2.77b) can be written as

$$dN/dt = k'NG(N/\theta') + N\delta F \tag{2.79b}$$

with

$$\theta' = \theta[1 + (a/k)]^{1/\nu}, \qquad k' = a + k. \tag{2.79c}$$

FIG. 4. The graph of an example of a 12-species ecology. If species i either feeds on species j or is eaten by j, a bond connects points i and j.

This generalization (2.79a) is also equivalent to the Morse potential since (on the assumption that

$$\langle F(t) \rangle = 0)$$

$$W(V) = -\nu \exp(\nu V) + k[1 - \exp(\nu V)]^2 \sigma^{-2} \quad (2.80a)$$

$$= A[\exp(2\nu x) - 2 \exp(\nu x)] + k\sigma^{-2}, \quad (2.80b)$$

where now

$$x = V - V^*, \qquad \exp(\nu V^*) = 1 + \nu\sigma^2/2k, \quad (2.80c)$$

$$A = k\sigma^{-2}(1 + \tfrac{1}{2}\nu\sigma^2 k^{-1})^2. \quad (2.80d)$$

The function Φ defined by

$$\Psi(V, t) = \Phi \exp\left[-\tfrac{1}{2}k(k\sigma^2 + E)t\right] \quad (2.81)$$

leads to

$$(\sigma^2/k)\Phi_{xx} + \{E - A[\exp(2\nu x) - 2 \exp(\nu x)]\}\Phi = 0 \quad (2.82)$$

which is the Schrödinger equation again for a Morse potential. Indeed, if we replace νx by x and σ^2/k by $(\nu\sigma)^2/k$, the analysis from (2.71)–(2.76) is immediately applicable. α as defined by (2.63) has the value ν.

IV. Equilibrium Theory

We now return to the Volterra equations in their original form and refrain from replacing the sum in (2.4) by a random function. A rather detailed analysis can be made of equilibrium populations $\{q_j\}$ by setting $\dot{N}_j = 0$ in the basic equation (1.2). This analysis is important because, as already shown in Sec. 1, the equilibrium population of a given species is the long time average of its population. This conclusion is not vitiated even by the inclusion of the Verhulst term [see Eq. (1.41) and the discussion following (1.44)]. Further, the calculation of equilibrium numbers can be used to develop the criteria for the stability of a given assembly of interacting species. For example, if by solving (1.6) we find that one or more of q's are negative, then the system is unstable. To show this we use the definition (1.46) for G'. In the absence of the Verhulst term, G' is a constant of motion, similar to G for the case of all q's positive. However, it is no longer true that each G_j' is bounded and positive for, if $q_j < 0$, i.e., $s_j = -1$, $G_j' \rightarrow -\infty$ as $v_j \rightarrow -\infty$ ($N_j \rightarrow 0$). Let $q_j < 0$. If none of the species disappear, i.e., N_j's are bounded away from zero, then each G_j' is bounded and, if so, then from the argument of Sec. 1

$$\bar{N}_j = q_j \qquad \text{for all } j. \qquad (3.1)$$

Hence, if only one of the q's is negative, e.g., $q_j < 0$, the population of species j has to cross zero and we arrive at a contradiction. This can be resolved only if the jth species disappears. If there are more than one species with negative q's, we cannot tell which of the species will disappear. The indirect way to deal with this case is to eliminate one of the species with negative q from the system and then consider the stability. Most probably the species whose elimination yields a stable system will then disappear.

The above result for the disappearance of a species with negative q is true even in the presence of the Verhulst term. This is so because, from (1.47), $dG'/dt \leq 0$, i.e., $G'(t) \leq G'(0)$, and if none of the species disappears, G' will be bounded and the argument presented will go through.

For the calculation of equilibrium numbers and the understanding of their connections with the stability of a system, it is convenient to associate a graph with an "ecology" (i.e., a specified set of a_{ij}). We represent each of the species by a point and each pair of species which influence each other directly by a line or bond connecting the two species points. An example of such a graph is given in Fig. 4. At least one of the k_i's must be positive if the populations of all the species are not to die out. It is sometimes useful to indicate the connection of those species with $k_i > 0$ to the great nutrient reservoir (the earth, sun, very small organisms which are not enumerated, etc.) by a dotted line to the ground. On this basis the big fish–little fish interaction graph would be given by Fig. 5(a).

We start our systematic discussion of equilibrium values of species populations by examining the case of three species. Then Eq. (1.6) has the form

$$q_1[\beta_1 k_1 \qquad + a_{12}q_2 + a_{13}q_3] = 0, \qquad (3.2)$$

$$q_2[\beta_2 k_2 + a_{21}q_1 \qquad + a_{23}q_3] = 0, \qquad (3.3)$$

$$q_3[\beta_3 k_3 + a_{31}q_1 + a_{32}q_2 \qquad] = 0. \qquad (3.4)$$

If one of the species, say $q_1 \equiv 0$, vanishes, then the other equilibrium populations are given immediately with $q_3 = \beta_2 k_2 / a_{32}$ and $q_2 = \beta_3 k_3 / a_{23}$. Since the only interesting case is one in which q_3 and q_2 are nonnegative, k_2 and a_{32} must have the same sign, as must k_3 and a_{23}. Hence k_2 and k_3 must have opposite signs. In view of the importance of signs, we add another convention to our graphs. When i feeds on j, we direct an arrow toward i on the bond connecting the points representing the species. Then the $n=2$ little fish–big fish case has the diagram shown in Fig. 5(b). The arrows give the direction of "material flow."

Let us seek a solution of (3.2)–(3.4) for which none of the q_j's vanish. Then the q_j factors on the left of each equation can be dropped. In order for this type of solution to exist, the determinant of the coefficients of

FIG. 5. Two-species graph. The dotted line indicates that species 2 feeds off the large natural reservoir and species 1 feeds only on 2. The arrows indicate the direction of "mass" flow.

the q_j's must not vanish. That determinant is

$$\begin{vmatrix} 0 & a_{12} & a_{13} \\ a_{21} & 0 & a_{23} \\ a_{31} & a_{32} & 0 \end{vmatrix} = a_{12}a_{23}a_{31} + a_{13}a_{32}a_{21}.$$

In view of the antisymmetry of the a_{ij}'s, this determinant vanishes, so that we have the interesting result (already known to Volterra) that there is no equilibrium population distribution between three species such that the population of all the species is finite and nonvanishing.

Since in this discussion we postulated that no species vanished at equilibrium, one way we can avoid having an equilibrium with a finite population of each species is to allow at least one to become infinite. When such a situation arises, one can no longer neglect the Verhulst term in (1.41). Let us suppose that species 3 is the only one for which k_j is positive. Then Eq. (3.4) becomes

$$\beta_3 k_3 (1 - q_3/\theta_3) + a_{31}q_1 + a_{32}q_2 = 0. \qquad (3.5)$$

Now consider the diagrams of Figs. 6(a), 6(b), and 6(c). Clearly, in Fig. 6(a), species 1 would vanish because it is eaten by 2 with no source to supply it. Hence the problem would reduce to a two-species problem and the discussion below (3.4) would apply.

In Fig. 6(b), $a_{31}=a_{13}=0$ so that our full set of equations would be

$$\beta_3 k_3 (1-q_3/\theta_3) + a_{32}q_2 = 0, \qquad (3.6a)$$

$$k_1\beta_1 + a_{12}q_2 = 0, \qquad (3.6b)$$

$$k_2\beta_2 + a_{21}q_1 + a_{23}q_3 = 0, \qquad (3.6c)$$

with

$$a_{32}<0, \qquad a_{12}>0, \qquad k_1\beta_1<0 \quad \text{and} \quad k_2\beta_2<0, \quad k_3\beta_3>0. \qquad (3.7)$$

We then have the equilibrium population

$$q_2 = k_1\beta_1/a_{21}>0, \qquad (3.8a)$$

$$q_3 = \theta_3(1 - a_{32}k_1\beta_1/a_{12}k_3\beta_3), \qquad (3.8b)$$

$$q_1 = -(k_2\beta_2/a_{21}) + (a_{23}/a_{12})\theta_3(1 - a_{32}k_1\beta_1/a_{12}k_3\beta_3). \qquad (3.8c)$$

If we have

$$(a_{32}k_1\beta_1/a_{12}k_3\beta_3)<1, \qquad (3.9)$$

then $q_3>0$. The second term in q_1 is also positive while the first term is negative. The ultimate fate of species 1 then depends on whether or not

$$(a_{23}/a_{12})\theta_3(1 - a_{32}k_1\beta_1/a_{12}k_3\beta_3) > (k_2\beta_2/a_{21}). \qquad (3.10)$$

If it is, then species 1 survives. If it is not, then the equilibrium population of species 1 is negative so that, from any initial distribution, it will pass zero, the point of the vanishing of the species in its trajectory toward the equilibrium point.

The ecology of Fig. 6(c) can be discussed in a similar

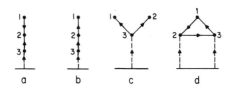

FIG. 6. Some graphs involving three interacting species.

44

way. The basic equations for equilibrium are (3.5) and

$$k_2\beta_2 + a_{23}q_3 = 0, \qquad (3.11a)$$

$$k_1\beta_1 + a_{13}q_3 = 0, \qquad (3.11b)$$

with

$$k_2\beta_2 < 0; \; k_1\beta_1 < 0; \; a_{23} > 0 \quad \text{and} \quad a_{13} > 0. \quad (3.12)$$

Hence, we find

$$q_3 = k_2\beta_2/a_{32} > 0 \quad \text{and} \quad q_3 = k_1\beta_1/a_{31}. \quad (3.13)$$

Generally these two equations are inconsistent; hence the hypothesis that there exists an equilibrium solution in which no species vanishes is false so that at least one has to vanish. In the *special* case

$$k_2\beta_2 a_{31} = k_1\beta_1 a_{32}, \qquad (3.14)$$

the two species 1 and 2 behave as though they are a single species and can form an equilibrium system with 3. Under this condition the system is equivalent to a two-species system.

Qualitatively it is not surprising that the ecology corresponding to Fig. 6(c) is generally unstable.

Both "1" and "2" nibble on "3" in a manner that is generally uncorrelated. Let us suppose that the death rate constant of 1 is smaller than that of 2. In the absence of 1, the population of 2 and 3 would oscillate. But now, when the population of both 3 and 2 are both low in a state such that 3 would start to recover in the absence of too many preying 2's, 1 with its smaller time constant would continue to attack 3 until either 2 or 3 disappeared. If 2 disappeared first, then 1 and 3 would form an oscillating two-species ecology. If 3 disappears, then both 1 and 2 would also die out. These implications come under a beautiful "ecological exclusion principle" known as Volterra–Lotka principle, according to which two closely similar species will not both indefinitely be able to occupy essentially the same ecological niche, but that the slightly more "successful" of the two will eventually completely supplant the other (Kerner, 1961, and the references therein). The reader might find it interesting to make an analysis of graph 6(d).

It can be shown that the determinant of any anti-symmetrical matrix of an odd order vanishes. This is related to the facts that the eigenvalues of an anti-symmetric matrix are purely imaginary and that they occur in pairs, one being the complex conjugate of the other. In the case of an odd order matrix, the only way this condition can be satisfied is to have one eigenvalue zero. Since the determinant of the matrix is the product

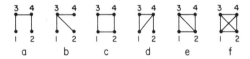

FIG. 7. All the connected graphs involving four interacting species.

of all the eigenvalues, it must then vanish. This means that in every Volterra ecology of an odd number of species, at least one must eventually die out or that at least one species would grow indefinitely in the absence of the Verhulst term. In the latter case, the Verhulst saturation term would have to be included in the manner discussed above for the three-species case. We develop the general theory after we complete our discussion of the ecology of an even number of species. We first examine in special cases the necessary condition for the existence of stable populations in the absence of a Verhulst term.

When n is even, say, $2N$, the necessary condition for the existence of a set of finite nonvanishing solutions of (1.6) is

$$D_{2N} = \begin{vmatrix} 0 & a_{12} & a_{13} & \cdots & a_{1,2N} \\ a_{21} & 0 & a_{23} & \cdots & a_{2,2N} \\ \cdots & \cdots & \cdots & \cdots & \cdots \\ a_{2N,1} & a_{2N,2} & a_{2N,3} & \cdots & 0 \end{vmatrix} \neq 0. \quad (3.15)$$

46

The determinant of an antisymmetric matrix A is a perfect square, and, indeed, its square root is an object called a Pfaffian (Caianiello, 1959; Montroll, 1964) with

$$D_{2N}^{1/2} = \text{Pf } A = \begin{vmatrix} a_{12} & a_{13} & a_{14} & \cdots & a_{1,2N} \\ & a_{23} & a_{24} & \cdots & a_{2,2N} \\ & & & & \vdots \\ & & & & a_{2N-1,2N} \end{vmatrix} \quad (3.16a)$$

$$= \sum \delta_p \ a_{p_1 p_2} \ a_{p_3 p_4} \ \cdots \ a_{p_{2N-1}, p_{2N}} \tag{3.16b}$$

$$p_1 < p_2, \quad p_3 < p_4, \quad p_5 < p_6, \cdots \text{ and } p_1 < p_3 < p_5 < \cdots, \tag{3.16c}$$

where the summation extends over all permutations of the integers $1, 2, \cdots, 2N$ which satisfy conditions (3.16c). The signature δ_p is $+1$ if $(p_1, p_2, \cdots, p_{2N})$ is an even permutation of the first $2N$ integers, and -1 if it is an odd permutation. When $N = 2$ (four species), we have

$$D_4 = (\text{Pf } A)^2 = (a_{12}a_{34} - a_{13}a_{24} + a_{14}a_{23})^2. \tag{3.17}$$

The equilibrium numbers in the case $n = 4$ are easily shown to be

$$q_1 = (k_2\beta_2 a_{34} + k_3\beta_3 a_{42} + k_4\beta_4 a_{23})/\text{Pf } A$$

$$= \begin{vmatrix} k_2\beta_2 & k_3\beta_3 & k_4\beta_4 \\ & a_{23} & a_{24} \\ & & a_{34} \end{vmatrix} /\text{Pf } A, \quad (3.18a)$$

$$q_2 = (k_1\beta_1 a_{43} + k_3\beta_3 a_{14} + k_4\beta_4 a_{31})/\text{Pf } A, \tag{3.18b}$$

$$q_3 = (k_1\beta_1 a_{24} + k_2\beta_2 a_{41} + k_4\beta_4 a_{12})/\text{Pf } A, \tag{3.18c}$$

$$q_4 = (k_1\beta_1 a_{32} + k_2\beta_2 a_{13} + k_3\beta_3 a_{21})/\text{Pf } A. \tag{3.18d}$$

Similar expressions can be derived for the general case

of an even number of species. This will be done later in this section. All q_j's can always be expressed as a ratio of two Pfaffians.

All possible diagrams (without arrows) which involve four connected species are given in Fig. 7. Equation (3.17) tells us which of these diagrams corresponds to the vanishing of one species. In cases (a)–(f), respectively, the Pfaffians, Pf A, are

(a) $-a_{13}a_{24}$ (b) 0

(c) $a_{12}a_{34} - a_{13}a_{24}$ (d) $-a_{13}a_{24} + a_{14}a_{23}$

(e) $a_{12}a_{34} - a_{13}a_{24}$ (f) $a_{12}a_{34} - a_{13}a_{24} + a_{12}a_{23}$.

$$(3.19)$$

Hence, with the exception of case (b), there is some possibility that there exist appropriate nonvanishing a_{jk} such that nonvanishing finite equilibrium populations exists for all species even in the absence of the Verhulst terms.

In order for physically reasonable nonvanishing solutions to exist for the basic equilibrium equation, all equilibrium populations q_j must be nonnegative. This puts certain restrictions on the ranges of the a_{jk}'s. Let us first consider case (a). Then from (3.18), with $a_{12} \equiv a_{23} \equiv a_{14} \equiv 0$, we have

$$q_1 = (k_2\beta_2 a_{34} + k_3\beta_3 a_{42})/a_{31}a_{24}, \qquad (3.20a)$$

$$q_2 = (k_1\beta_1 a_{43} + k_4\beta_4 a_{31})/a_{31}a_{24}, \qquad (3.20b)$$

$$q_3 = k_1\beta_1/a_{31} \quad \text{and} \quad q_4 = k_2\beta_2/a_{42}. \qquad (3.20c)$$

There are a number of diagrams which express the manner in which graph (a) is applicable. One or more of our four species can feed on the nutrient reservoir with a number of possibilities of whether i eats j, or j eats i. Some of these possibilities are exhibited in Fig. 8. Consider first case (i). We ask for a set of conditions such that each $q_j > 0$. Our arrangement of arrows imply

48

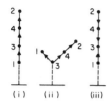

FIG. 8. Some of the graphs involving four interacting species. The graphs represent some of the interactions with the nutrient reservoir.

$$k_1>0, \qquad k_2<0, \qquad k_3<0, \quad \text{and} \quad k_4<0$$

$$a_{31}>0, \qquad a_{43}>0, \quad \text{and} \quad a_{24}>0.$$

From these conditions it is clear that $q_3>0$, $q_4>0$, and $q_1>0$. The stationary population q_2 of species 2 can be positive only if

$$k_1\beta_1a_{43} > k_4\beta_4a_{13}. \qquad (3.21)$$

Hence once the diagram with the arrow arrangement (i) is presented to us, an equilibrium population distribution exists as long as (3.21) is satisfied.

Case (ii) is characterized by

$$k_1<0, \qquad k_2<0, \qquad k_3>0, \quad \text{and} \quad k_4<0,$$

while

$$a_{13}>0, \qquad a_{43}>0, \quad \text{and} \quad a_{24}>0.$$

The conditions for this system to have an equilibrium population are

$$\beta_1k_1a_{34} > -k_4\beta_4a_{13},$$

$$k_3\beta_3a_{24} > k_2\beta_2a_{34}.$$

Intuitively one would expect species 4 and 2 to disappear under the conditions of diagram (iii) so that some q_k would be negative. The characteristics of (iii) are

$$k_1>0, \qquad k_3<0, \qquad k_2<0, \qquad k_4<0;$$

$$a_{31}>0, \qquad a_{34}>0, \qquad a_{42}>0.$$

For these conditions, $q_4<0$. Hence no suitable equilibrium conditions with four species exist. As shown in the beginning of the section, if one of the q's is negative, the species corresponding to $q<0$ will disappear. Thus species 4 will disappear. Since species 2 will then be isolated, it will also disappear.

The reader can easily work out the conditions for the existence of positive equilibrium populations for various other diagrams involving four species.

These ideas can be generalized to the case of $2N$ species. For this purpose, the expansion of the Pfaffian by "line" is useful. The hth "line" is defined as the set of elements a_{jk} which have h as one of the subscripts. In terms of line 1, the expansion of the Pfaffian (3.16a) is

$$\text{Pf } A \equiv (1, 2, \cdots, 2N)$$

$$= \sum_{k=2}^{2N} (-1)^k a_{1k}(2, \cdots, k-1, k+1, \cdots, 2N), \quad (3.22)$$

where $(2, \cdots, k-1, k+1, \cdots, 2N)$ represents the Pfaffian of a's with the first subscript starting with 2 and the second ending with $2N$, and with subscript k missing. For example, when $N=2$, we have

$$\text{Pf } A = (1, 2, 3, 4) = a_{12}(3, 4) - a_{13}(2, 4) + a_{14}(2, 3)$$

$$= a_{12}a_{34} - a_{13}a_{34} + a_{14}a_{23}$$

as required.

The general set of linear equations (1.6) for equilibrium populations $\{q_j\}$ can be solved by Cramer's rule. After some elementary manipulation, using (3.22), one finds

$$q_i \text{ Pf } A = (-1)^{i+1} \sum_{j \neq i} k_j \beta_j$$

$$\times (j+1, j+2, \cdots, 2N, 1, 2, \cdots, i-1, i+1, \cdots, j-1),$$

$$(3.23)$$

where the Pfaffian on the right starts with subscripts $j+1$ and ends with $j-1$ with j and i omitted. For example, when $N = 3$, we have

$$q_1 \operatorname{Pf} A = k_2\beta_2(3, 4, 5, 6) + k_3\beta_3(4, 5, 6, 2) + k_4\beta_4(5, 6, 2, 3)$$
$$+ k_5\beta_5(6, 2, 3, 4) + k_6\beta_6(2, 3, 4, 5)$$
$$= k_2\beta_2(3, 4, 5, 6) - k_3\beta_3(2, 4, 5, 6) + k_4\beta_4(2, 3, 5, 6)$$
$$- k_5\beta_5(2, 3, 4, 6) + k_6\beta_6(2, 3, 4, 5)$$

$$= \begin{vmatrix} k_2\beta_2 & k_3\beta_3 & k_4\beta_4 & k_5\beta_5 & k_6\beta_6 \\ & a_{23} & a_{24} & a_{25} & a_{26} \\ & & a_{34} & a_{35} & a_{36} \\ & & & a_{45} & a_{46} \\ & & & & a_{56} \end{vmatrix},$$

$$q_2 \operatorname{Pf} A = - \begin{vmatrix} k_1\beta_1 & k_3\beta_3 & k_4\beta_4 & k_5\beta_5 & k_6\beta_6 \\ & a_{13} & a_{14} & a_{15} & a_{16} \\ & & a_{34} & a_{35} & a_{36} \\ & & & a_{45} & a_{46} \\ & & & & a_{56} \end{vmatrix}, \text{ etc. } (3.24)$$

There are two advantages of writing the equilibrium populations in terms of Pfaffians. First, it is easier to construct explicit expressions for $\{q_i\}$ for any number of species than it would be if we used determinants. Also, if one knows which a_{ij}'s are zero, it is easier to decide if $\det A = 0$, i.e., to see if a set of nonvanishing q_i's exist which are a solution of (1.6). We now develop the latter point further and develop a scheme for making a quick decision to see whether or not $\operatorname{Pf} A = 0$.

We are concerned only with interconnected graphs. There must be some path along which one can go from any point to any other point. We start our expansion by choosing a point which is attached to only one other point, say for species 1, which we postulate to be connected only to species 2. Then if we expand Pf A in terms of line 1, the result would be a_{12} multiplied by a new Pfaffian which we would again reduce by seeking other loose ends in the diagram which represents our system. The final unfactorable Pfaffian would have to be examined to see whether or not it vanishes.

To clarify this procedure, consider the diagram of Fig. 4. The reader can easily construct the Pfaffian. If one expands successively by line 2, line 3, line 4, and line 5, which correspond to loose ends in the figure, one finds

$$\text{Pf } A = a_{12}(-a_{37})a_{48}(-a_{59}) \begin{vmatrix} a_{6,10} & 0 & 0 \\ & a_{10,11} & 0 \\ & & a_{11,12} \end{vmatrix}$$

$$= a_{12}a_{37}a_{48}a_{59}a_{6,10}a_{11,12} \neq 0.$$

It is interesting to note that if the doubly connected ring $(10, 11, 12, 8, 7)$ is cut by setting $a_{11,12}=0$, the Pfaffian vanishes, while this is not the case when the cut is made between 10 and 11 since $a_{10,11}$ does not enter into the formula.

By inserting a bond between 5 and 6, one can no longer factor the Pfaffian into a product of a_{jk}'s. Let us in this case expand the Pfaffian successively along lines 2, 3, and 4. Then we obtain

$$\text{Pf } A = a_{12}(-a_{37})a_{48} \begin{vmatrix} a_{56} & a_{59} & 0 & 0 & 0 \\ 0 & a_{6,10} & 0 & 0 \\ & a_{9,10} & a_{9,11} & 0 \\ & & a_{10,11} & 0 \\ & & & a_{11,12} \end{vmatrix}$$

$$= a_{12}(-a_{37})a_{48}a_{11,12}[a_{56}a_{9,10} - a_{59}a_{6,10}]$$

which will not vanish unless $a_{56}a_{9,10} = a_{59}a_{6,10}$, a singular situation.

One can derive the conditions for all q_i to be positive in the above two cases, but of course it requires a little more effort than it did in our cases with four species.

We should point out that associating a graph with an ecology and then determining whether the Pfaffian is zero or not has interesting implications about the stability of the population when new species are introduced. To illustrate let us consider a system of eight species. Let us number them 5, 6, 7, 8, 9, 10, 11, and 12 and let them be connected as in Fig. 4, with the exception that 11 and 12 are not connected. Since the Pfaffian of this population is not zero, in general, this population is stable. Suppose we introduce two new species, 1 and 2, with the interactions in the manner shown in Fig. 4 (i.e., 2 interacts with 1 only, and 1 with 6 only). One can easily see that the Pfaffian is still not zero and, in general, the system of 10 species should be stable. However, if we introduce two other species (say 3 and 4) such that they do not interact with each other but interact with the two species (7 and 8) of the original eight species, the Pfaffian is zero and the system of 10 species is unstable.

Let us now consider the general case in which det a_{ij} vanishes in the absence of the Verhulst term. Through the introduction of the Verhulst term, we can find the equilibrium distribution if one exists or determine which species vanishes if the equilibrium distribution does not exist.

We first discuss the case of an odd number of species, say, $(2n+1)$, in which only one, namely, species $(2n+1)$, is connected to the nutrient reservoir. Species $(2n+1)$ is the only one which does not depend on any other of our selected species for survival. As in the three-species case, we must include the Verhulst term in the equation obtained by setting $dN_{2n+1}/dt=0$ and letting $N_{2n+1} \equiv q_{2n+1}$. One then finds that

$$0 = k_{2n+1}\beta_{2n+1}(1 - q_{2n+1}/\theta_{2n+1}) + \sum_{j=1}^{2n} a_{2n+1,j}q_j = 0, \quad (3.25)$$

where θ_{2n+1} represents the saturation population of species $(2n+1)$ in the absence of all others. The generalization of (1.6) for $i=1, 2, \cdots, 2n$ is

$$k_i'\beta_i' + \sum_{j=1}^{2n} a_{ij}q_j = 0, \qquad i=1, 2, \cdots, 2n, \quad (3.26a)$$

with

$$k_i'\beta_i' = k_i\beta_i + a_{i,2n+1}q_{2n+1}. \qquad (3.26b)$$

Hence if we can determine q_{2n+1} separately, all the other equilibrium populations are given by Pfaffians analogous to (3.24) with the $k_i\beta_i$ in (3.24) replaced by $k_i'\beta_i'$.

The calculation of q_{2n+1} is performed by writing (3.26) in the alternative form

$$-k_i\beta_i = \sum_{j=1}^{2n+1} a_{ij}q_j, \qquad i=1, 2, \cdots, 2n, \quad (3.27a)$$

and (3.25) as

$$-k_{2n+1}\beta_{2n+1} = \sum_{j=1}^{2n+1} a_{2n+1,j}q_j \qquad (3.27b)$$

with the definition

$$a_{2n+1,2n+1} \equiv -k_{2n+1}\beta_{2n+1}/\theta_{2n+1} \equiv x. \qquad (3.28)$$

The determinant of the coefficients of q_j has the form

$$f(x) \equiv \det a_{ij} \equiv \begin{vmatrix} 0 & a_{12} & \cdots & a_{1,2n+1} \\ a_{21} & 0 & \cdots & a_{2,2n+1} \\ \cdots & \cdots & \cdots & \cdots \\ a_{2n+1,1} & \cdots & \cdots & x \end{vmatrix}. \qquad (3.29)$$

If we set x equal to zero, $\det a_{ij}$ becomes an anti-symmetrical determinant with an odd number of rows and columns which, as we mentioned earlier, vanishes and we find

$$f(0) = 0.$$

By expanding the determinant by the bottom row, we find

$$f(x) = x \begin{vmatrix} 0 & a_{12} & \cdots & a_{1,2n} \\ a_{21} & 0 & \cdots & a_{2,2n} \\ \cdots & \cdots & \cdots & \cdots \\ a_{2n,1} & a_{2n,2} & \cdots & 0 \end{vmatrix} + \text{const.} \quad (3.30)$$

However, since $f(0) = 0$, the constant must vanish. Hence, from (3.29), we have

$$\det a_{ij} = x(\text{Pf } A)^2 = -\{k_{2n+1}\beta_{2n+1}/\theta_{2n+1}\} (\text{Pf } A)^2, \quad (3.31)$$

where $\text{Pf } A$ is the Pfaffian of the antisymmetric matrix of $2n$ rows and columns.

The final equilibrium population of species $(2n+1)$ is then

$$q_{2n+1} = - \begin{vmatrix} 0 & a_{12} & a_{1,2n} & -k_1\beta_1 \\ a_{21} & 0 & a_{2,2n} & -k_2\beta_2 \\ \cdots & \cdots & \cdots & \cdots \\ a_{2n+1,1} & a_{2n+1,2} & a_{2n+1,2n} & -k_{2n+1}\beta_{2n+1} \end{vmatrix}$$

$$\times \theta_{2n+1}/k_{2n+1}\beta_{2n+1}(\text{Pf } A)^2$$

$$= \begin{vmatrix} k_1\beta_1 & k_2\beta_2 & k_3\beta_3 & \cdots & k_{2n+1}\beta_{2n+1} \\ & a_{12} & a_{13} & \cdots & a_{1,2n+1} \\ & & a_{23} & \cdots & a_{2,2n+1} \\ & & & \cdots & \cdots \\ & & & & a_{2n,2n+1} \end{vmatrix}$$

$$\times \theta_{2n+1}/k_{2n+1}\beta_{2n+1} \, \text{Pf } A. \quad (3.32)$$

As was mentioned above, once q_{2n+1} is known, it can be substituted into (3.26b) so that $k_i'\beta_i'$ are known. Then from (3.26a), $q_1, q_2, \cdots, q_{2n}$ can be determined from generalizations of (3.24) in which $k_i\beta_i$ are replaced by $k_i'\beta_i'$.

When several k_i are positive, it can be shown that

$$q_i\Delta = (i+1, i+2, \cdots, n, 1, \cdots, i-1)E, \quad (3.33)$$

where

$$E = \sum_{j=1}^{n} k_j\beta_j(j+1, j+2, \cdots, n, 1, \cdots, j-1), \quad (3.34a)$$

$$\Delta = -\sum_i (k_i\beta_i/\theta_i)(i+1, i+2, \cdots, n, 1, \cdots, i-1)^2$$

$$+O(1/\theta_i\theta_l), \quad (3.34b)$$

where the summation over i extends over all i for which $k_i > 0$. Generally, the saturation levels θ_i would be expected to be much greater than populations which could be achieved under competitive conditions. Hence the terms of $O(1/\theta_i\theta_l)$ can be neglected, compared with those of order $(1/\theta_i)$.

In the expression (3.33) for q_i, the only quantity which depends on the Verhulst term is Δ, which from (3.34b) is always negative. Therefore, the sign of q_i as determined by keeping the Verhulst terms is the same as in the limit of Verhulst term going to zero. If from (3.33) and (3.34), we find that all the q's are positive, then the system will be stable. (Of course, we will need some Verhulst terms to have a finite value for q's.) If, on the other hand, we find that only one of the q's, e.g., q_i, is negative, then as argued in the beginning of this section, the ith species will disappear. If more than one of the q's are negative, we can not determine directly which of the species will disappear. The indirect way to deal with the problem is to eliminate one of the species with negative q and consider the stability of the remaining system anew. The species whose elimination will lead to the stable system will be the one which will disappear. Since, in general, E is nonzero, one of the q's, say q_i, will be zero, provided the Pfaffian in (3.33) is zero. In this case one has to examine the higher order terms and then determine whether q_i is positive or negative. The chances are that the ith species will survive because the Pfaffian in (3.33) equal to zero implies that the system without ith species forms an unstable system.

For an even number of species when $\det a_{ij} = 0$, one can proceed basically in the same fashion as for the odd number of species. However, to obtain q_i's, one must have two species with nonvanishing Verhulst terms. This can be seen by an equation similar to (3.29) for an even number of species. If only one diagonal term is nonzero, $\det (a_{ij})$ is still zero because the coefficient of the diagonal term in the expansion of the determinant is an antisymmetric determinant of odd order. We may add that we were unable to get an expression as simple as (3.33) for a general system of $2n$ species with an arbitrary number of species having nonzero Verhulst terms.

V. Time-Dependent Fluctuations in Population

It was mentioned in the previous section that systems composed of an odd number of species either reach an equilibrium set of populations or decay into systems containing an even number of species. Therefore, if one wishes to discuss fluctuations, it is sufficient to investigate the general set of Volterra equations for an even number of species. We shall consider the time dependence of the population of various species when the deviation from equilibrium populations is small. This case is discussed for two reasons:

(i) Since, experimentally, it is difficult to measure k_i and a_{ij}, the next best thing one might attempt is to see how much qualitative information can be derived about an ecological situation in terms of statistical properties of the a_{ij}'s and k_i's. Kerner (1957, 1959) has done some elegant work in this direction by applying the techniques of statistical mechanics to the Volterra model of competing species. His ideas have been extended by Goodwin (1963) to a system of interacting biochemical oscillators and of simultaneously growing cells (Goodwin, 1970) and by Cowan (1968) to the nervous system. A gap in these investigations is the justification of the application of the techniques of statistical mechanics to the respective biological situations. For example, Kerner (1957) (see Sec. 1) recognized that Volterra's system of differential equations admits a Liouville theorem (when $\log \{N_i\}$ are used as variables) and that there is a constant of motion. Hence he can define a microcanonical ensemble such that the time averages over a single system can be equated to the phase averages over the microcanonical ensemble. This last equality (an ergodic theorem) has been shown to be true only for the averages of N_i. Its general validity, for arbitrary functions of one or more N_i, is not established. Kerner then proceeds to define a canonical ensemble by introducing a quantity Θ analogous to the temperature of a physical system and assumes that microcanonical ensemble averages are the same as the canonical ensemble averages. The only justification for the introduction of the canonical ensemble is that it works in physics and, therefore, with luck, it should work here also. We know that its justification in physics is very tricky and that it is true only if certain conditions are satisfied by the system (Khinchin, 1959). The study of the time-dependent fluctuations in populations lets us find conditions, if any, under which certain techniques of statistical mechanics can be applied to the system of interacting species, i.e., conditions under which Kerner's treatment is valid. We will find these conditions, if any, in this section. A similar analysis can be made for the system of interacting biochemical oscillators, the nervous system or growing cells.

(ii) If one is concerned with the stability of an ecology under various disturbances, this small deviation regime is sufficient to tell whether a specified perturbation leads to an instability even though the understanding of the full development of the instability follows only by application of the complete nonlinear equations. This small deviation regime also allows a comparison of the stability of two systems in the sense of rarity of explosions and vanishing of species.

We will emphasize only the first reason in detail in this section and postpone the question of stability to the next section.

Let us write

$$N_i(t) = q_i[1 + \delta_i(t)]. \tag{4.1}$$

Then, if each δ_i is small, (1.2) becomes

$$\beta_i \dot{\delta}_i = \sum_{j=1}^{n} a_{ij} q_j \delta_j. \tag{4.2}$$

60

If we let

$$x_i = \delta_i (q_i \beta_i)^{1/2}, \tag{4.3}$$

$$C_{ij} = (q_i/\beta_i)^{1/2} a_{ij} (q_j/\beta_j)^{1/2} = -C_{ji}, \tag{4.4}$$

then (4.2) becomes

$$\dot{x}_i = \sum_j C_{ij} x_j \tag{4.5a}$$

or

$$\dot{x}(t) = Cx(t), \tag{4.5b}$$

where $x(t)$ is a column vector with components $x_j(t)$ and C is an $n \times n$ antisymmetric matrix with C_{ij} as elements.

It is well known that the characteristic values of an antisymmetric matrix such as C are purely imaginary and that they occur in pairs so that, if one is $i\omega_l$, another is $-i\omega_l$. Let A_{il} be the ith element of the lth characteristic vector (corresponding to the characteristic value λ_l) of C, i.e.,

$$\sum_k C_{ik} A_{kl} = \lambda_l A_{il}. \tag{4.6}$$

Let A be the matrix whose elements are A_{il} and $A^\dagger$ one whose elements are A_{li}^*. If we normalize the characteristic vectors properly, we can choose

$$A^\dagger A = I, \quad \text{i.e., } \sum_l A_{li}^* A_{lj} = \delta_{ij}, \tag{4.7a}$$

where $A^\dagger$ is the Hermitian conjugate of A, and I is the identity matrix. Taking the complex conjugate of (4.6) and using the identity $\lambda_l^* = -\lambda_l$, we get

$$\sum_k C_{ik} A_{kl}^* = -\lambda_l A_{il}^*. \tag{4.7b}$$

Thus A_{kl}^* is the kth element of the characteristic vector which corresponds to the characteristic value $-\lambda_l$. Further, using the identity $C_{ij} = -C_{ji}$, we get

$$\sum_k (A^\dagger)_{lk} C_{ki} = \lambda_l (A^\dagger)_{li}. \tag{4.8}$$

Therefore $(A^\dagger)_{il}$ is the ith element of the lth characteristic row vector corresponding to the characteristic value λ_l.

The solution of (4.5) can now be written as

$$x_i(t) = \sum_l \alpha_l A_{il} \exp(t\lambda_l), \qquad (4.9)$$

where α_l are constants to be determined from the application of the orthogonality relationship (4.7) to $x_i(0)$, i.e.,

$$\sum_i x_i(0) A_{im}{}^* = \alpha_m. \qquad (4.10)$$

Substituting (4.10) into (4.9), we get

$$x_i(t) = \sum_{lj} A_{il} A_{jl}{}^* x_j(0) \exp(t\lambda_l). \qquad (4.11)$$

This equation thus gives the time evolution of the population near equilibrium. Since q_i's are functions of k_i and a_{ij}, from (4.4) the C_{ij}'s are functions of k_i, β_i, and a_{ij}, the parameters describing the growth and interaction of the various species. Thus, in principle, A and λ_l, and from (4.11) for the given initial values of N_i, $x_i(t)$ too can be expressed in terms of k_i, β_i, and a_{ij}. If the population is far away from the equilibrium, we have to use a perturbation theory. Such a perturbation theory is due to Kryloff and Bogoliuboff (1947). Its application to two-species cases is described in Bak (1963) and, for a system of anharmonic oscillators, in Ford (1961) and Ford and Waters (1963). In this perturbation theory, the expansion parameter is proportional to $x_i(0)$. Thus any statement about average of any function of N_i's should be true for all the terms in the perturbation theory involving different powers of $x_i(0)$. In particular, it should be true if we calculate N_i using only first order terms, i.e., (4.11). From (4.11), since λ_i's are imaginary, we have

$$[\![x_i(t)]\!] = 0 = [\![y_i(t)]\!]$$

which is what we should expect since $[\![N_i]\!] = q_i$. Also,

$E\{N_i\}$ and $\langle N_i \rangle$ both are equal to q_i. Therefore, the ergodic theorem is true for N_i. However, from (1.31b), $E\{x_ix_j\}$ and $\langle x_ix_j \rangle$ $(i \neq j)$ are both zero. If the ergodic theorem is true in general, $[\![x_ix_j]\!]$ should also be zero. But, from (4.11), since x_j is real, we have

$$[\![x_ix_j]\!] = [\![x_ix_j{}^*]\!]$$
$$= \sum_{mqkl} A_{il}A_{kl}{}^*A_{jm}{}^*A_{qm}[\![\exp\{(\lambda_l+\lambda_m{}^*)t\}]\!]x_k(0)x_q(0).$$

Since λ_l's are imaginary, we find

$$[\![x_ix_j]\!] = \sum_{klq} A_{il}A_{kl}{}^*A_{jl}{}^*A_{ql}x_k(0)x_q(0)$$
$$= \sum_l A_{il}A_{jl}{}^* \mid \sum_k A_{kl}x_k(0) \mid^2$$
$$\neq 0.$$

Thus the ergodic theorem for arbitrary function of x_i's for an arbitrary system of interacting species is not valid. We will now find the conditions under which not only $[\![x_ix_j]\!] = 0$, but time averages of all other functions of x_i's are equal to ensemble averages.

Let us first find the probability distribution of $x_i(t)$, for a fixed i, as a function of time when (a) it is known at time $t = 0$ that x_i has the value $x_i(0)$, and (b) equal probability is given to every initial distribution of other x_j's which are consistent with

$$G_0 = \sum_j \beta_j[N_j(0) - q_j]^2/2q_j = \tfrac{1}{2}\sum_j x_j{}^2(0) = \text{const.}$$
$$(4.12)$$

This is of course the small deviation from the equilibrium version of (1.9b) when $t = 0$. We define R^2 by

$$\tfrac{1}{2}\sum_{j\neq i} x_j{}^2(0) = \tfrac{1}{2}R^2. \qquad (4.13)$$

The problem posed above is that of finding the statistics of

$$Y(t) = x_i(t) - M_{ii}(t)x_i(0) = \sum_{j\neq i} M_{ij}(t)x_j(0), \quad (4.14)$$

where M_{ij} is defined by

$$x_i(t) = \sum_j M_{ij}(t) x_j(0), \qquad (4.15a)$$

i.e.

$$M_{ij}(t) = \sum_l A_{il} A_{jl}{}^* \exp(t\lambda_l), \qquad (4.15b)$$

when at $t=0$, all sets of $\{x_j(0)\}$ (with $j \neq i$) which are consistent with

$$R^2 = \sum_{j \neq i} x_j{}^2(0) = \sum_j x_j{}^2(0) - x_i{}^2(0) \qquad (4.16)$$

are given equal weight. This problem has been solved by Mazur and Montroll (1960) in the context of vibrations of crystal lattices. When n is large, the probability distribution of $Y(t)$ is Gaussian (for all $n > 1$, see Montroll (1961)):

$$f[Y(t)] = g[x_i(t) \mid x_i(0)] = \{[n/(2\pi)^{-1}]^{1/2}/\sigma R\}$$

$$\times \exp\{-n[x_i(t) - M_{ii}(t) x_i(0)]^2/2R^2\sigma^2\}, \quad (4.17a)$$

where

$$\sigma^2 = \sum_{j \neq i} M_{ij}{}^2(t) = \sum_j M_{ij}{}^2(t) - M_{ii}{}^2(t). \quad (4.17b)$$

We notice from (4.15b) that

$$\sum_j M_{ij}{}^2(t) = \sum_{l,m} A_{il} A_{jl}{}^* A_{im} A_{jm}{}^* \exp[(\lambda_l + \lambda_m)t].$$

$$(4.18)$$

Since the summation over m extends over all characteristic values $\{\lambda_m\}$, we see that from (4.7) we can replace λ_m by $-\lambda_m$ if, at the same time, we replace A_{im} by $A_{im}{}^*$ and $A_{jm}{}^*$ by A_{jm}. Hence, in view of (4.7), we have

$$\sum_j M_{ij}{}^2(t) = \sum_{j,l,m} A_{il} A_{jl}{}^* A_{jm} A_{im}{}^* \exp[t(\lambda_l - \lambda_m)]$$

$$= \sum_l A_{il} A_{il}{}^* = 1 \qquad (4.19)$$

and, therefore, from (4.17b),

$$\sigma^2 = 1 - M_{ii}^2(t). \qquad (4.20)$$

It remains to consider $M_{ii}(t)$. Since the characteristic values $\lambda_m = i\omega_m$ and $-i\omega_m$ both appear, one can write

$$M_{ii}(t) = 2 \sum_{\alpha=1}^{N} A_{i\alpha} A_{i\alpha}^* \cos t\omega_\alpha, \qquad N = \tfrac{1}{2}n. \quad (4.21)$$

If all the ω_α are distinct, $M_{ii}(t)$ is almost periodic so that, if it achieves any value once, it will achieve it an infinite number of times.

In view of the normalization of the $A_{i\alpha}$, (4.7a), each $A_{i\alpha}$ is $O(N^{-1/2})$ so that $| A_{i\alpha} |^2 = O(N^{-1})$. Since $M_{ii}(0) = 1$, $\sigma^2(0) = 0$. Now let us write (4.21) as

$$M_{ii}(t) = (2/N) \sum_{\alpha} | A_{i\alpha} N^{1/2} |^2 \cos t\omega_\alpha. \quad (4.22)$$

If at a given time the various cosines are completely out of phase so that there are roughly as many positive as negative ones, one might consider the sum to be that of N random independent variables, each $O(1)$. Then by the central limit theorem for the sum of random independent variables the expected value of the sum would be $O(N^{1/2})$ so that $M_{ii}(t) = O(N^{-1/2})$, and, as the number of interacting species becomes large, $M_{ii}(t)$ would become small so that the term $M_{ii}(t)x_i(0)$ could be neglected in (4.17a). In that case, $Y(t)$ would have a Gaussian distribution which is independent of $x_i(0)$. This is in accordance with Kerner's distribution (1957) for an ecology which suffers only small displacements from equilibrium.

The above heuristic remarks can be put on a more rigorous basis by phrasing the discussion of $M_{ii}(t)$ in a somewhat different manner. Since $M_{ii}(t)$ is an almost periodic function, we know from the work of Wintner (1933) that we can rigorously find the fraction of time spent by $M_{ii}(t)$ within a given interval ξ and $\xi + d\xi$. Since the qualitative behavior of $M_{ii}(t)$ is the same as that of its average over i, we will, for mathematical convenience, deal with this average

$$\rho_N(t) = n^{-1} \sum_{i=1}^{n} M_{ii}(t)$$

$$= N^{-1} \sum_{\alpha=1}^{N} \cos \omega_\alpha t,$$

$$N = n/2, \tag{4.23}$$

where the last step follows from (4.21). It is known that if we assume ω_α to be linearly independent, it is possible to define a distribution function $\psi(\xi)$ for $\rho_N(t)$ defined by the following equation:

$$\psi(\xi)d\xi = \lim_{T \to \infty} \text{meas } \{\xi < \rho_N(t) < \xi + d\xi; T\}/T, \tag{4.24}$$

where $\{\xi < \rho_N(t) < \xi + d\xi; T\}$ denotes the set of all those points t for which both the inequalities $\xi < \rho_N(t) < \xi + d\xi$, $t < T$ are satisfied, and meas $\{\xi < \rho_N(t) < \xi + d\xi; T\}$ is the Lebesgue measure of this set. In more physical terms $\psi(\xi)$ measures the probability density of finding ρ with the value ξ. It is shown in Wintner (1933) that for $\rho_N(t)$ as given above, the function $\psi(\xi)$ is given by

$$\psi(\xi) = (2\pi)^{-1} \int_{-\infty}^{\infty} \exp\,(-i\xi S)[J_0(S)]^N \, dS. \tag{4.25}$$

We will evaluate this quantity when $\xi < bN^{1/2}$, where b is some preassigned number $O(1)$ and show that sufficient information can be extracted from this region for our purpose.

We know we can write $J_0(S)$ as

$$J_0(S) = \{1 - \tfrac{1}{4}(S/2)^4 + O(S^6)\} \exp\,(-S^2/4). \tag{4.25'}$$

Hence, on making this expansion, we can write

$$\psi(\xi) = (2\pi)^{-1} \int_{-\infty}^{\infty} \exp\,(-i\xi S)\, \exp\left[-\left(\frac{S^2}{4}\right) N \right]$$

$$\times \{1 - \tfrac{1}{4}N(\tfrac{1}{2}S)^4 + \text{ higher order terms}\} \, dS. \tag{4.25''}$$

We write $\xi = bN^{1/2}$

$$\eta = \xi S = SbN^{1/2}.$$

With this substitution we have

$$\psi(\xi) = (2\pi)^{-1}(bN^{1/2})^{-1}\int \exp(-i\eta) \exp(-\eta^2/4b^2)$$
$$\times \{1 - \tfrac{1}{4}N(\eta/bN^{1/2})^4 + \cdots\} \, d\eta.$$

Hence for large N, b finite, we get

$$\psi(\xi) = (2\pi bN^{1/2})^{-1} \int_{-\infty}^{\infty} \exp\left(-i\eta - \frac{\eta^2}{4b^2}\right) d\eta$$

$$= (\pi N)^{-1/2} \exp(-\xi^2/N). \qquad (4.26)$$

We next try to find the probability that $|\rho_N(t)|$ has a value greater than $bN^{1/2}$. This is given by

Prob $\{|\rho_N(t)| > bN^{1/2}\}$

$$= 1 - (\pi N)^{-1/2} \int_{-bN^{1/2}}^{bN^{1/2}} \exp\left(-\frac{\xi^2}{N}\right) d\xi$$

$$= 1 - \pi^{-1/2} \int_{-b}^{b} \exp(-\eta^2) \, d\eta = 1 - E_2(b), \quad (4.27)$$

where $E_2(b)$ is the standard error integral. For small values of b, this expression approaches zero. For example, for $b = 2$, the above probability is 0.005. Since the region in which the integration is carried out is confined within the region $\pm bN^{1/2}$, our asymptotic probability density function is accurate, and without investigating regions of the order of N, we can say that $\rho_N(t)$ is almost always confined to the region $\pm bN^{1/2}$, b any preassigned small number. Hence $\rho_N(t)$ is almost always confined to the noise region and in the limit $n \to \infty$, $\rho_N(t) \to 0$. In the limit $n \to \infty$ the distribution function of the ith species about its equilibrium value q_i is then [see (4.17a), (4.13), (4.3), and (4.1)]

$$p(N_i) = (2\pi\beta_i/Iq_i)^{-1/2} \exp[-\beta_i(N_i - q_i)^2/2Iq_i] \quad (4.28)$$

since the noise band becomes vanishingly small. The parameter $I = R^2/n$ has the value given in (4.13). When written in terms of populations, it has the form

$$I = n^{-1} \sum x_j^2(0)$$

$$= n^{-1} \sum (\beta_i/q_i)[N_i(0) - q_i]^2 = 2G_0/n, \quad (4.29)$$

where (G_0/n) is our constant of motion per species [see Eq. (4.12)] in the small vibration regime. This is just the canonical distribution conjectured by Kerner (1957) for this regime.

These results can be generalized to a selected set of m out of n species where $m \ll n$. The joint distribution function of m species is to be found from the joint distribution of $Y_1(t), Y_2(t), \cdots, Y_m(t)$, where

$$Y_1(t) = x_1(t) - M_{11}(t)x_1(0) - M_{12}(t)x_2(0)$$

$$- \cdots - M_{1m}(t)x_m(0) = \sum_{j \neq 1,2,\cdots,m} M_{ij}(t)x_j(0),$$

$$Y_2(t) = x_2(t) - M_{21}(t)x_1(0) - M_{22}(t)x_2(0)$$

$$- \cdots - M_{2m}(t)x_m(0) = \sum_{j \neq 1,2,\cdots,m} M_{2j}(t)x_j(0), \text{ etc.}$$

$$(4.30)$$

The joint characteristic function of $Y_1(t), Y_2(t), \cdots, Y_m(t)$ is

$$\langle \exp [i \sum_1^m \alpha_\nu Y_\nu(t)] \rangle$$

$$= \langle \exp \{i \sum_{j \neq 1,\cdots,m} [\alpha_1 M_{1j}(t) + \cdots + \alpha_m M_{mj}(t)]x_j(0)\} \rangle,$$

$$(4.31)$$

where all sets of $x_j(0)$ which lie on the $N - m$ dimensional hypersphere

$$\tfrac{1}{2} \sum_{j \neq 1,2,\cdots,m} x_j^2(0) = \tfrac{1}{2}R^2. \quad (4.32)$$

If m is fixed and N is very large, our required characteristic function is known to be Gaussian, i.e.,

$$\exp\left(-\tfrac{1}{2}\sigma^2 R^2/n\right), \tag{4.33a}$$

where

$$R^2 = \sum_{j \neq 1,2,\cdots,m} x_j^2(0), \tag{4.33b}$$

$$\sigma^2 = \sum_{j \neq 1,2,\cdots,m} \left[\alpha_1 M_{1j}(t) + \alpha_2 M_{2j}(t) + \cdots + \alpha_m M_{mj}(t)\right]^2$$

$$= \sum_j \left[\alpha_1 M_{1j}(t) + \cdots + \alpha_m M_{mj}(t)\right]^2$$

$$- \left[\alpha_1 M_{11}(t) + \alpha_2 M_{21}(t) + \cdots + \alpha_m M_{m1}(t)\right]^2$$

$$- \left[\alpha_1 M_{12}(t) + \alpha_2 M_{22}(t) + \cdots + \alpha_m M_{m2}(t)\right]^2$$

$$\cdots$$

$$- \left[\alpha_1 M_{1m}(t) + \alpha_2 M_{2m}(t) + \cdots + \alpha_m M_{mm}(t)\right]^2. \tag{4.33c}$$

Since

$$\sum_j M_{ij} M_{kj} = \delta_{ik}, \tag{4.34}$$

we see that

$$\sigma^2 = \alpha_1^2 + \alpha_2^2 + \cdots + \alpha_m^2$$

$$- \left[\alpha_1 M_{11}(t) + \cdots + \alpha_m M_{m1}(t)\right]^2$$

$$- \cdots$$

$$- \left[\alpha_1 M_{1m}(t) + \cdots + \alpha_m M_{mm}(t)\right]^2. \tag{4.35}$$

The joint distribution function of $Y_1, Y_2, \cdots, Y_m$ is obtained by taking the Fourier transform of the characteristic function

$$f[Y_1, Y_2, \cdots, Y_m] = \frac{1}{(2\pi)^m} \int_{-\infty}^{\infty} \cdots \int \exp\left(-i\alpha \cdot Y\right)$$

$$\times \exp\left(-\tfrac{1}{2}\sigma^2 R^2/n\right) d\alpha_1 \cdots d\alpha_m, \tag{4.36}$$

where

$$\alpha \cdot Y = \alpha_1 Y_1 + \cdots + \alpha_m Y_m, \qquad (4.37)$$

$$\sigma^2 = \alpha' \cdot A \cdot \alpha, \qquad (4.38)$$

A being the matrix of the coefficients of $\alpha_i \alpha_j$ of (4.35). For example, when $m = 2$, we have

$$\sigma^2 = \alpha_1{}^2 (1 - M_{11}{}^2 - M_{12}{}^2) - 2\alpha_1 \alpha_2 M_{21} M_{11}$$
$$- 2\alpha_2 \alpha_1 M_{12} M_{22} + \alpha_2{}^2 (1 - M_{22}{}^2 - M_{21}{}^2). \quad (4.39)$$

The well-known formula for the Fourier integral of a Gaussian is

$$\frac{1}{\pi^{m/2}} \int_{-\infty}^{\infty} \cdots \int_{-\infty}^{\infty} d^m \alpha \, \exp \, (i\alpha \cdot y) \, \exp \, (-\alpha' B \alpha)$$
$$= (\det A)^{-1/2} \exp \left[-(x^2/2) \right], \quad (4.40a)$$

where, if B^{-1} is the inverse of the matrix B,

$$x^2 = \tfrac{1}{2}(Y' \cdot B^{-1} \cdot Y). \qquad (4.40b)$$

Hence (4.36) becomes

$$f(Y_1, Y_2, \cdots, Y_m)$$
$$= \exp \left\{ -\tfrac{1}{4}(Y' B^{-1} Y) \right\} / 2^m \pi^{m/2} (\det B)^{1/2}. \quad (4.41)$$

Now let

$$B = \tfrac{1}{2}(A R^2/n) \quad \text{and} \quad B^{-1} = 2n A^{-1}/R^2, \quad (4.42a)$$

$$\det B = (R^2/2n)^m \det A. \qquad (4.42b)$$

Hence we find

$$f(Y_1 \cdots Y_m) = \frac{\exp \, (-\tfrac{1}{2} n Y' A^{-1} Y/R^2)}{(2\pi R^2/n)^{m/2} (\det A)^{1/2}}. \quad (4.43)$$

In the special case, $m = 2$, we have

$$a_{11} = 1 - M_{11}{}^2 - M_{12}{}^2, \qquad a_{12} = 2M_{21} M_{11}, \qquad (4.44a)$$

$$a_{21} = -2M_{12} M_{22}, \qquad a_{22} = 1 - M_{22}{}^2 - M_{21}{}^2, \quad (4.44b)$$

$$A^{-1} = \begin{pmatrix} a_{22} & -a_{12} \\ -a_{21} & a_{11} \end{pmatrix} \Big/ (a_{11} a_{22} - a_{12} a_{21}). \quad (4.45)$$

The theorem which was discussed in connection with Eq. (4.21) implies that, as $n \to \infty$, the terms $M_{ij}(t) = O(n^{-1/2}) \to 0$ so that the matrices A and A^{-1} become identity matrices. In this limit, $f(Y_1, \cdots, Y_m)$ factors into a product of m one-species distribution functions of the form (4.28) when transformed back to population variables.

Thus if

$$M_{ii}(t) \to 0 \qquad \text{as } t \to \infty, \qquad (4.46)$$

the distribution function of one or more species about their equilibrium value is a Gaussian distribution, the same as the canonical distribution (1.34) for small deviation from the equilibrium value.

To prove that the canonical average of a function of N_i's is equal to the time average, i.e., to prove the ergodic theorem, we first show that the canonical average is equal to the microcanonical average and that the latter average is equal to the time average. To show the equality of the first two averages, we note (a) that a canonical average of any function of y_i can be written in terms of $\langle y_i{}^2 \rangle$ (see Sec. 1) and (b) that if (1.32) is satisfied, then the relation between $E\{y_i{}^p\}$ and $E\{y_i{}^2\}$ is the same as that between $\langle y_i{}^p \rangle$ and $\langle y_i{}^2 \rangle$ [see (1.33) and (1.39)]. Therefore, if we can show that

$$\langle y_i{}^2 \rangle = E\{y_i{}^2\} \quad \text{or} \quad \langle x_i{}^2 \rangle = E\{x_i{}^2\} \qquad (4.47)$$

and that (1.32) is true, then the equality of the first two averages is proved. But, from (4.28), we have

$$\langle x_i{}^2 \rangle = I = 2G_0/n \qquad (4.48)$$

and from (1.31c) and (4.3) we have

$$E\{x_i{}^2\} = \theta_2 = \text{const.} \qquad (4.49)$$

Therefore, from (4.29), we find

$$E\{x_i{}^2\} = 2G_0/n \qquad (4.50)$$

which proves (4.47) and, hence, if we also show that

(1.32) is satisfied, then the equality of canonical and microcanonical averages is proved. To prove this equality with the time averages and (1.32), we first discuss the physical significance of the quantity $M_{ij}(t)$ which has been central to so much of our discussion. The physical significance is clear if we consider the correlation function

$$\rho_n(i, k; t, \tau)$$

$$= E\{x_i(t+\tau)x_k^*(t)\}/[E\{x_i^2(0)\}E\{x_k^2(0)\}]^{1/2}, \quad (4.51)$$

where the averaging is to be done over the initial conditions

$$E\{x_j(0)x_k(0)\} = \theta_2\delta_{jk}. \tag{4.52}$$

Equation (4.52) follows from (4.49) and the assumption that the populations of different species are initially uncorrelated. From (4.11), (4.7a), and (4.52), we have

$$E\{x_i(t+\tau)x_k^*(t)\} = E\{\sum_{ljms} A_{il}A_{jl}^*x_j(0)$$

$$\times \exp[(t+\tau)\lambda_l]A_{km}^*A_{sm}x_s(0)\exp(t\lambda_m^*)\}$$

$$= \sum_{ljms} A_{il}A_{jl}^*A_{sm}A_{km}^*$$

$$\times \exp[t(\lambda_l+\lambda_m^*)+\tau\lambda_l]E\{x_j(0)x_s(0)\}$$

$$= \theta_2\sum_{ljm} A_{il}A_{jl}^*A_{km}^*A_{jm}$$

$$\times \exp[t(\lambda_l+\lambda_m^*)+\tau\lambda_l]$$

$$= \theta_2\sum_l A_{il}A_{kl}^*\exp(\tau\lambda_l)$$

since $\lambda_l^* = -\lambda_l$. From (4.51), this implies that independently of t

$$M_{ik}(\tau) \equiv \rho_n(i, k; \tau), \tag{4.53a}$$

where $M_{ik}(\tau)$ is the correlation function defined above. M_{ii} is thus a normalized autocorrelation function, i.e.,

$$M_{ii}(\tau) = \rho_n(i, \tau) = E\{x_i(t+\tau)x_i(t)\}/E\{x_i^2(0)\}.$$

$$(4.53b)$$

To prove the ergodic theorem for a microcanonical ensemble, we make use of a theorem on ergodic functions (Khinchin, 1959; Mazur and Montroll, 1960) according to which, if

$$\rho(\tau) = E\{f_i(t+\tau)f_i^*(t)\} \to 0 \qquad \text{as } \tau \to \infty, \quad (4.53c)$$

then the function $f_i(t)$ of the variable $x_i(t)$ is ergodic. If (4.46) is satisfied, then from (4.53c) x_i is ergodic. We had already shown this rigorously in Sec. 1. To show the ergodicity of a general function, we consider the following two normalized autocorrelation functions:

$$P_n(i, t) = E\{[x_i^2(t) - \theta_2][x_i^2(0) - \theta_2]\}/E\{[x_i^2(0) - \theta_2]^2\}$$

$$(4.54a)$$

$$Q_n(i, j, t)$$
$$= E\{x_i(t)x_j(t)x_i(0)x_j(0)\}/E\{x_i^2(0)\}E\{x_j^2(0)\},$$

$$i \neq j, \quad (4.54b)$$

Substituting for $x_i(t)$ from (4.11), and using (4.7a) and (4.52), one can easily show that for large n,

$$P_n(i, t) = [\rho_n(i, t)]^2 = M_{ii}^2(t) \qquad (4.55a)$$

and

$$Q_n(i, j, t) = \rho_n(i, t)\rho_n(j, t)$$
$$= M_{ii}M_{jj}, \qquad i \neq j. \qquad (4.55b)$$

Thus if (4.46) is satisfied, both P_n and $Q_n \to 0$ as $t \to \infty$, and from the theorem mentioned above, $x_i^2(t)$ and $x_i(t)x_j(t)$, $i \neq j$, are both ergodic. Further $Q_n \to 0$ implies $E\{x_ix_j\} = 0 = E\{x_i\}E\{x_j\}$. By considering function $Q_n(i, j, k, \cdots, t)$, defined similarly to (4.54b), one can show that $Q_n \to 0$, which implies $E\{x_ix_j\cdots\} = E\{x_i\}E\{x_j\}\cdots$. Generalizing the argument further will imply (1.32), thus proving the ergodic theorem for both microcanonical and canonical averages. Thus, if the number of species is large, the ergodic theorem is true, at least in the linear approximation. This condition is met in our ecological system because the number of species is perhaps several million or more. Hence we may apply statistical mechanics with some confidence. It should be noted that the above-mentioned conditions are only necessary conditions for the nonlinear case and need not be sufficient. To determine whether they are or are not we must investigate the ergodic theorem for each term in the perturbation theory of the type mentioned earlier in the section. This is beyond the scope of this paper.

It is interesting to find the manner in which $x_i^2(t)$ achieves its equipartition value $2G_0/n$. Since we have

$$\langle x_i^2(t) \rangle_t = \langle [x_i(t) - x_i(0)\rho_n(i, t)]^2 \rangle_t$$
$$+ 2x_i(0)\rho_n(i, t) \langle [x_i(t) - x_i(0)\rho_n(i, t)] \rangle_t$$
$$+ x_i^2(0)\rho_n^2(i, t), \quad (4.56)$$

where $\langle \rangle_t$ denotes the average over the distribution (4.17a), from (4.17a) we have

$$\langle x_i^2(t) \rangle_t = 2n^{-1}G_0[1 - \rho_n(i, t)]^2 + x_i^2(0)\rho_n^2(i, t). \quad (4.57)$$

This follows from the fact that the first average on the right of (4.56) is just the dispersion of the distribution function (4.17a) and the second one vanishes. As $t \to \infty$, $\langle x_i^2(t) \rangle_t \to 2G_0/n$, while as $t \to 0$, $\langle x_i^2(t) \rangle_t \to x_i^2(0)$ since $\rho_n(i, t) \to 0$ as $t \to \infty$ and $\rho_n(i, t) \to 1$ as $t \to 0$.

Further, from (4.48), if two systems of populations with n_1 and n_2 species and with their values Θ_1 and Θ_2 are connected to each other (through some prey–predator interaction), then the value of the combined system is

$$\Theta = (\Theta_1 n_1 + \Theta_2 n_2)/(n_1 + n_2). \quad (4.58)$$

In the end we would like to point out that the statistical method of Wintner (1933) used in evaluating the properties of $\rho_N(t)$ could be used directly to evaluate the distribution for $x_i(t)$ which themselves are almost periodic functions of time. From (4.15a) and (4.15b) we have

$$x_i(t) = \sum_{l,j} A_{il}A_{jl}{}^* \exp(\lambda_l t)x_j(0). \quad (4.59)$$

Coupling terms of λ_l of the form $\pm i\omega_l$, we get

$$X_i(t) = \sum_{l=1}^{N} \left[p_{il} \exp\,(i\omega_l t) + p_{il}{}^* \exp\,(-i\omega_l t) \right]$$

$$= 2 \sum_{l=1}^{N} |\,p_{il}\,|\,\cos\,(\omega_l t + \delta_l) = \sum_{l=1}^{N} r_{il} \cos\,(\omega_l t + \delta_l)$$

(4.60)

with $p_{il} = |\,p_{il}\,| \exp\,(i\delta_l)$, where

$$r_{il} = 2 |\,p_{il}\,| = 2\,|\, \sum_{j=1}^{n} A_{il} A_{jl}{}^* x_j(0)\,|. \qquad (4.61)$$

We now define the function $\psi_i(\xi)$ by

$$\psi_i(\xi)\,d\xi = \lim_{T \to \infty} \text{meas}\,\{\xi < x_i(t) < \xi + d\xi;\, T\}/T, \quad (4.62)$$

where $\{\xi < x_i(t) < \xi + d\xi;\, T\}$ denotes the set of all those points t for which both the inequalities $\xi < x_i(t) < \xi + d\xi$, $t < T$ are satisfied, and meas $\{\xi < x_i(t) < \xi + d\xi;\, T\}$ is the Lebesgue measure of this set. It is shown in Wintner (1933) that $\psi_i(\xi)$ is given by

$$\psi_i(\xi) = (2\pi)^{-1} \int_{-\infty}^{\infty} \exp\,(-i\xi S) \sum_{l=1}^{N} J_0(r_{il} S)\,dS. \quad (4.63)$$

By an analysis similar to that used for the derivation of $\rho_N(t)$, it can be shown that to a first approximation it is valid to replace $J_0(r_{il} S)$ by $\exp\,(-\tfrac{1}{4} r_{il}{}^2 S^2)$. Hence we have

$$\Psi_i(\xi) = (2\pi)^{-1} \int_{-\infty}^{\infty} \exp\,(-i\xi S)\,\exp\,(-\tfrac{1}{4} S^2 \sum_{l=1}^{N} r_{il}{}^2)\,dS.$$

(4.64)

Now we define

$$r_i{}^2 = N^{-1} \sum_{l=1}^{N} r_{il}{}^2. \qquad (4.65)$$

Hence we have

$$\psi_i(\xi) = (2\pi)^{-1} \int_{-\infty}^{\infty} \exp\,(-i\xi S)\,\exp\left[-N r_i{}^2 \left(\frac{S^2}{4} \right) \right] dS.$$

(4.66)

We put $\xi S = \eta$ to get

$$\psi_i(\xi) = (2\pi)^{-1}$$

$$\times \left\{ \xi^{-1} \int_{-\infty}^{\infty} \exp\,(-i\eta)\,\exp\left[-Nr_i^2\left(\frac{\eta^2}{4\xi^2}\right) \right] d\eta \right\}.$$

Putting $\xi = bN^{1/2}$, we get

$$\psi_i(\xi) = (2\pi\xi)^{-1} \int_{-\infty}^{\infty} \exp\,(-i\eta)\,\exp\left[-\left(\frac{r_i^2}{4b^2}\right)\eta^2 \right] d\eta$$

$$= (1/\pi^{1/2})\,(b/r_i\xi)\,\exp\,(-2\xi^2/nr_i^2)$$

$$= [1/(2\pi)^{1/2}\sigma_i]\,\exp\,(-\xi^2/2\sigma_i^2) \qquad (4.67)$$

with

$$\sigma_i^2 = (nr_i^2/4). \qquad (4.68)$$

Obviously we have

$$\sigma_i^2 = \tfrac{1}{4}nr_i^2 = \tfrac{1}{2}\sum_{l=1}^{n/2} r_{il}^2$$

$$= 2\sum_{l=1}^{n/2} p_{il}p_{il}^* = \sum_{l=1}^{n} p_{il}p_{il}^* \qquad (4.69)$$

if we now extend back the sum over all n. Thus we get

$$\sigma_i^2 = \sum_{l=1}^{n}\sum_{j=1}^{n}\sum_{k=1}^{n} A_{il}A_{il}^*A_{jl}^*A_{kl}x_j(0)x_K(0) = [\![x_i^2]\!]. \qquad (4.70)$$

We see that each $x_i(t)$ is distributed in a Gaussian manner with its own σ_i. In a given physical situation, the initial conditions are totally unknown and it is appropriate to use an average value σ in place of σ_i, the average being taken over all the species. If we do this, we obtain

$$\sigma = n^{-1}\sum_{i=1}^{n} \sigma_i = n^{-1}\sum x_k^2(0) = \frac{2G_0}{n} \qquad (4.71)$$

agreeing with expression (4.68). We thus get back the distribution which we derived on a more physical basis.

VI. Diversity and Stability in Ecological Systems

We now shall use the results of the previous section to study diversity and stability of species in an ecological system. Diversity and stability are much talked about, but poorly defined, concepts in ecology. Recently a whole symposium at Brookhaven National Laboratory was planned by the organizers "to examine the meaning of these two terms as used by students of natural systems···" (Woodwell and Smith, 1969). By glancing through the papers published in the report of the symposium, one can see that the definitions are quite subjective.

In a rough sense, diversity is the number of species per unit area. The diversity is known to have changed during the evolution of our present ecological system. Based on geological and fossil records, it is believed that there were times when the diversity was "richer" than the present one and there were times when it was "poorer." The basic questions are: what determines the diversity and can we account for the present diversity?

Stability can be put into three categories (Preston, 1969): (a) physiographic stability—the stability of a particular geographic region; (b) local and global stability (constancy) of the number of species, and, (c) stability of the number of individuals of a particular species in the sense of rarity of the crashes or explosions. Perhaps the answer to the question about diversity posed in the preceding paragraph is that the diversity at any time is that for which the stability of all the three types is maximum. The present section is devoted to the investigation of the relation between diversity and stability.

For simplicity, we limit ourselves to the stability as defined above in the third category. The problem then is to investigate the type of species which will form a stable population. Given an ensemble of M species, a species i being characterized by the parameters a_{ij} (with j ranging through all species which are connected to i) and k_i, one can choose a variety of subsets of n species out of the M and compare the stability of an ecology of one of the subsets with that of another. Perhaps nature even works this way. After many thousands of years of evolution, one would expect to find in isolated regions an ecology that is more stable than others which might have developed. In comparing the stability of various possible ecologies, one might compare those which had certain similar macroscopic properties which depend on the equilibrium populations. Two such macroscopic properties which appear frequently in the literature are the biomass and productivity which at equilibrium are defined by

$$B = \sum_i q_i \beta_i \qquad (5.1)$$

and

$$P = \tfrac{1}{2} \sum_{ij} |a_{ij}| \, q_i q_j. \qquad (5.2)$$

The biomass has an obvious meaning, while the productivity is the rate of flow of mass between species at equilibrium.

One way to investigate the stability of a number of species is through the autocorrelation function $\rho_n(i, t)$ [Eq. (4.53b)] of the population of various species. In a completely stable assembly in which each species approaches an equilibrium population independent of the initial distribution, the autocorrelation function would vanish after a long time. In our model, each population varies around its equilibrium population with an average amplitude that depends on the total number of species. One measure of the stability of an ecology would be the frequency with which the normalized autocorrelation function would pass some preassigned level of deviation from its equilibrium value, zero. Fluctuations of animal populations as a measure of community stability were suggested by McArthur (1955).

Since the level of stability of the ecology should not depend on any one species, we will choose as our measure of stability the frequency with which the average autocorrelation function

$$\rho_n(t) \equiv n^{-1} \sum_{i=1}^{n} \rho_n(i, t) \tag{5.3}$$

crosses a preassigned level. Those ecologies for which this frequency is very high will be considered to be less stable than those for which it is low.

From (5.3), (4.52b), (4.21), and (4.7a), we have

$$\rho_N(t) = N^{-1} \sum_{\alpha=1}^{N} \cos \omega_\alpha t. \tag{5.4}$$

Let us define $L(u)$ to be the mean frequency (averaged over a very long time) with which $\rho_N(t)$ achieves the value u. As shown in Sec. 4, $\rho_N(t)$ is confined mostly to the noise range. We will be primarily interested in values of u in this region, i.e., $u = cN^{-1/2}$ where $c = O(1)$ and is independent of N. As shown by Kac (1943; see also Montroll, 1961) we have

$$L(cN^{-1/2}) = (\omega_0/\pi) \exp(-c^2/2). \tag{5.5}$$

The frequency ω_0 is defined by

$$\omega_0{}^2 = N^{-1} \sum_{\alpha=1}^{N} \omega_\alpha{}^2. \tag{5.6}$$

Equation (5.5) is valid when

$$\lim_{n \to \infty} N^{-2} \sum_{\alpha=1}^{N} \omega_\alpha{}^4 = 0. \tag{5.7}$$

On the other hand, from (4.27), the mean frequency of

79

the achievement of a value α (with α close to 1) by $\rho_N(t)$ is (Slater, 1939)

$$L(\alpha) = (\omega_0/2\pi^{3/2})\{(1-\alpha)/\pi e\}^{1/2(N-1)}. \quad (5.8)$$

For large N this frequency is negligible. An important interpretation of this result is that, on the average, one has to wait a time which increases exponentially with the number of species n for an undisturbed ecology to suffer wild fluctuations outside of the noise range. This tells us that the more species one has, the more stable the ecology in that each species will tend to have very small fluctuations about its equilibrium population.

Most of the time $\rho_n(t)$ is restricted to a range $\pm cN^{-1/2}$ where $c \simeq O(1)$. For a given N and c, the stability will be great when $L(cN^{1/2})$ is small, i.e., when ω_0 is small, since the sum of the square of the eigenvalues of a matrix is the trace of the square of the matrix. We see from (4.4) and (4.5) that

$$\omega_0{}^2 = n^{-1} \sum_{ij} a_{ij}{}^2 q_i q_j (\beta_i \beta_j)^{-1}. \quad (5.9a)$$

A measure of stability would then be the magnitude of $\omega_0{}^2$. This gives a basis for the comparison of several ecological situations. That which yields the smallest value of ω_0 has the most stable population. It should be noted that our analysis depended on the conditions (5.7). This condition is satisfied if every species interacts with only a limited number of other species.

The rate constants $\{a_{ij}\}$ in Eq. (5.9a) and the equilibrium population $\{q_j\}$ are not independent parameters, but are related by (1.6). Hence, if one wishes to find the most stable ecology when some macroscopic constraints are applied, say,

$$F_\alpha(\{a_{ij}\}) = \mu_\alpha, \qquad \alpha = 1, 2, \cdots, s, \quad (5.9b)$$

the μ_α's being constant, then (5.9a) is to be minimized under these constraints using Lagrange multipliers. Let us suppose that in some sense the present distribution of species populations in isolated regions developed because they represent the most stable population relative to some restrictions of the form

(5.9b). As far as we can see, there is no *a priori* way of choosing these constraints. On this basis, the only course available to us is to make some guesses of restrictions and deduce the conditions on the a_{ij}'s which would lead to the greatest stability. We will consider several hypotheses here and deduce their consequences to indicate how one might proceed. The number of possibilities is large; we examine a few examples.

One of the simplest hypotheses is to assume (a) that the set of equilibrium populations is known (we know the present situation) and that the a_{ij}'s can have any real value (still with $a_{ij} = -a_{ji}$); (b) the network of interaction, the "food web" is fixed; (c) the productivity (5.2) is fixed; (d) for simplicity we choose $\beta_1 = \beta_2 = \cdots, \beta_n = 1$. In view of (1.6), once the q_j's and a_{ij}'s are chosen, the rate constants $k_1, k_2, \cdots, k_n$ become fixed. Since the k's do not appear explicitly in (5.9) nor in the expression for the productivity, we need not consider them unless we wish to find their explicit values after the a_{ij}'s are chosen to minimize ω_0^2. Once the q_i's are given, the biomass (5.1) is determined.

To achieve the minimization, we use the standard method of Lagrange undetermined multipliers, i.e., we minimize the expression

$$R_1 \equiv \sum_{i,j} |a_{ij}|^2 q_i q_j - \lambda(\tfrac{1}{2} \sum |a_{ij}| q_i q_j - P) \quad (5.10)$$

with respect to $|a_{ij}|$, keeping q's constant. Since q's are kept constant and a_{ij}'s are varied, from (1.6), k_i is not fixed. In other words, we are assuming that the growth rate of the species will change (presumably through the change in the environment) such that (1.6) is always satisfied. Thus a_{ij}'s obtained by minimizing R_1 will correspond to the conditions that productivity and q_i are fixed, but that the growth rates are changing. R_1 is minimum for $|a_{ij}|$ given by

$$\partial R_1 / \partial |a_{ij}| = 0 = 2 |a_{ij}| q_i q_j - \lambda q_i q_j, \qquad a_{ij} \neq 0 \quad (5.11)$$

or

$$|a_{ij}| = \lambda/2. \quad (5.12)$$

Substituting in (5.2), we get

$$4P = \lambda \sum_{i,j}' q_i q_j \equiv \lambda B', \tag{5.13}$$

where the prime over the summation indicates that the sum is to be taken over those i and j for which $a_{ij} \neq 0$. From (5.12) and (5.13),

$$|a_{ij}| = 2P/B'. \tag{5.14}$$

Therefore, the food web structure of maximum stability is that for which all the nonvanishing $|a_{ij}|$ are equal. If we make an additional assumption of $q_i \sim B/n$, then, from (5.13),

$$B' = (B^2/n^2) \sum_i \epsilon_i, \tag{5.15}$$

where $\epsilon_i (\ll n)$ denotes the number of species with which the species i interacts. If ϵ denotes the average ϵ_i, i.e.,

$$\epsilon = n^{-1} \sum \epsilon_i, \tag{5.16}$$

then from (5.14), (5.15), and (5.16), the maximum stability occurs for

$$|a_{ij}| = (2P/B^2)(n/\epsilon). \tag{5.17}$$

Substituting for $|a_{ij}|$ into (5.9), we get

$$\omega_0{}^2 = 4P^2/B^2\epsilon. \tag{5.18}$$

Thus the stability is positively correlated to the biomass and the average number of food links per species and negatively correlated to the productivity.

Before we study the stability under other fixed macroscopic conditions, we will briefly review the work of Leigh (1965, 1969), who employs a definition of stability similar to ours. He takes the stability of species i to be inversely proportional to the frequency with which $\log N_i/q_i = v_i$ crosses the line $v_i = d$, d being a constant. Within the linear approximation, this frequency can be expressed as a certain time integral. Since Leigh was unable to evaluate this time integral exactly, he replaced it by an integral over phase space of the variable $v_1 \cdots v_n$. On evaluating the phase integral approximately, the frequency of v_i crossing the line $v_i = d$ is

$$\omega_i = \pi^{-1} \{\sum_j a_{ij}{}^2 q_i q_j\}^{1/2} \exp\left(-q_i d^2/2\Theta\right). \quad (5.19)$$

Leigh then postulated that for maximum stability of the community, the average of this frequency, i.e.,

$$\omega = n^{-1} \sum_{i,j} \omega_i,$$

should be minimum, subject to the condition that P is constant. It turned out that he could not minimize under these conditions, so he restricted himself to the case of q_i fixed, i.e., biomass fixed. Even with these simplifications, the minimization could still not be performed and he hoped that the minimization of

$$J = \sum_{i,j} a_{ij}{}^2 q_i q_j$$

under the assumption of fixed productivity would attain the same end. The minimization is the same as that required for our analysis. However, in our definition of stability, J appears in a natural form rather than due to an approximation as in Leigh's definition. On minimization he gets the result that the stability is maximum for

$$|a_{ij}| = 2P/B^2, \qquad \text{all } i, j, \qquad (5.20)$$

rather than $|a_{ij}|$ given by (5.14) or (5.17). In other words, the food web structure of maximum stability is that in which every species feeds on all other species that do not feed on it. Substituting (5.20) into (5.19) and making the assumption that $q_i \sim B/n$, ω_i becomes

$$\omega_i = (2/\pi)(P/B) n^{-1/2} \exp\left(-q_i d^2/2\Theta\right). \quad (5.21)$$

Thus the stability is positively correlated to the number of species rather than to the average number of food links per species, as implied by (5.18). It should be noted that Leigh's result of all the a_{ij}'s nonvanishing and equal in magnitude is inconsistent with our formalism because then (5.7) is not satisfied and $L(CN^{-1/2})$ is no longer given by (5.5).

We now minimize J by keeping some other combination of macroscopic parameters (other than P and B) fixed. We will show that if we do so, all the nonvanishing $|a_{ij}|$ need not be equal. Suppose we keep both the biomass and the environment, i.e., all k_i's fixed. The proper quantity which has to be minimized is

$$R_2 = \sum_{i,j} a_{ij}^2 q_i q_j + \lambda (B - \sum q_i)$$
$$+ (- \sum k_i - 4 \sum_{i,j} a_{ij} q_j \mu_i), \quad (5.22)$$

where λ and $4\mu_i$'s are the undetermined multipliers. Differentiating (5.22) with respect to a_{ij} and q_i and equating the differentials equal to zero, we have

$$a_{ij} = \{ (\mu_i/q_i) - (\mu_j/q_j) \}, \quad \text{if } a_{ij} \neq 0, \quad (5.23a)$$

$$\sum_j^i a_{ij} q_j [a_{ij} + (2\mu_j/q_j)] = \lambda, \quad (5.23b)$$

where the i over the summation sign in (5.23b) denotes the sum over those j's for which $a_{ij} \neq 0$. Substituting (5.23a) into (5.23b), and (5.23a) into (1.6), we get

$$\sum_j^i \left\{ \left(\frac{\mu_i}{q_i} \right)^2 - \left(\frac{\mu_j}{q_j} \right)^2 \right\} q_j = \lambda, \quad i = 1, \cdots, n, \quad (5.24a)$$

$$\sum_j^i \left\{ \left(\frac{\mu_i}{q_i} \right) - \left(\frac{\mu_j}{q_j} \right) \right\} q_j = k_i, \quad i = 1, \cdots, n, \quad (5.24b)$$

$$\sum q_i = B. \quad (5.24c)$$

Equations (5.24a) and (5.24b) can, in principle, be solved for the $2n+1$ variables λ, μ_i's, and q_i's which, when substituted into (5.23a) will give a_{ij}'s for maximum stability. In general, clearly these a_{ij}'s are not equal and it is not possible to write a compact expression. The form will depend upon which of the a_{ij}'s and how many of them are zero. It should be noted that the form (5.23a) for a_{ij} implies that there will be one species which always feeds on others and is never eaten by any one of them and, also, a species which is always eaten by others and never eats any one of them. These two species are characterized, respectively, by the highest and lowest values of μ_i/q_i. If only the environment is fixed, then the corresponding results are obtained by putting $\lambda = 0$ in (5.22), (5.23b), and (5.24a), and eliminating (5.24c). We leave as an exercise for the reader the discussion of stability when P, B, and k_i's are all fixed.

VII. Volterra Equations with Random Rate Constants

All of our previous calculations have been made on the basis of constant "rate constants." One might expect the "rate constants" to be affected by changes in temperature, humidity, age distribution of various species, time of year, and other ecological factors. On this basis we assume that the a_{ij}'s are random variables. Then the N_j's are characterized by a probability distribution. We will derive a master equation for this distribution and show that, at equilibrium under certain conditions, this distribution has the Poisson form conjectured by Kerner (1957).

We start with Eq. (1.2):

$$\beta_i \frac{d \log N_i}{dt} = k_i \beta_i + \sum_{j=1}^{b} a_{ij} N_j \qquad (6.1)$$

and now consider the a_{ij} to be random variables with mean values $\bar{a}_{ij}$. We define a set of mean equilibrium populations $\{Q_j\}$ by

$$k_i \beta_i + \sum_{j=1}^{n} \bar{a}_{ij} Q_j = 0. \qquad (6.2)$$

We also define

$$V_j = \log (N_j/Q_j) \quad \text{or} \quad N_j = Q_j \exp (V_j). \quad (6.3)$$

Then one finds from (6.1), (6.2), and (6.3) that

$$\beta_i dV_i/dt = \sum_j Q_j [a_{ij} \exp (V_j - \bar{a}_{ij})], \qquad (6.4)$$

$$\beta_i dV_i/dt = \sum_j Q_j \bar{a}_{ij} [-1 + \exp (V_j)]$$

$$+ \sum_j Q_j \eta_{ij} \exp (V_j), \quad (6.5a)$$

where η_{ij} is the variation of a_{ij} from its mean value $\bar{a}_{ij}$,

$$a_{ij}(t) = \bar{a}_{ij} + \eta_{ij}(t), \quad (6.5b)$$

and

$$\langle \eta_{ij} \rangle = 0 \quad \text{and} \quad \eta_{ij} = -\eta_{ji}. \quad (6.5c)$$

In a small time Δt, the variation in V_i is, to within terms $O([\Delta t]^2)$,

$$\Delta V_i = \beta_i^{-1} \Delta t \sum_j Q_j \bar{a}_{ij} [-1 + \exp (V_j)]$$

$$+ \beta_i^{-1} \sum_j Q_j [\exp (V_j)] \int_t^{t+\Delta t} \eta_{ij}(t_1) \, dt_1$$

so that, if we average only the a_{ij}, we find

$$\langle \Delta V_i \rangle = \beta_i^{-1} \Delta t \sum_j Q_j \bar{a}_{ij} [-1 + \exp (V_j)]. \quad (6.6)$$

The average is calculated subject to the hypothesis that V_j is known to have the value $V_j(t)$ at time t. The fact that V_j depends on a_{ij} is irrelevant since we are only concerned with its average variation when $V_j(t)$ is specified. In averaging over $a_{ij} \exp (V_j)$ in the time interval Δt, the dependence on the variation of $\exp (V_j)$ is $O(\Delta t)$ compared with $\exp (V_j)$. Hence $\exp (V_j)$ is essentially constant during the averaging period.

We also see that

$$\Delta V_i \Delta V_k = (\Delta t)^2 \sum_{jl} Q_j Q_l \bar{a}_{ij} \bar{a}_{kl}$$

$$\times [-1 + \exp (V_j)][-1 + \exp (V_l)] \beta_i^{-1} \beta_k^{-1}$$

$$+ \beta_i^{-1} \beta_k^{-1} \Delta t \sum_j Q_j \bar{a}_{ij} [-1 + \exp (V_j)]$$

$$\times \sum_l Q_l[\exp\ (V_l)] \int_t^{t+\Delta t} \eta_{kl}(t_2)\ dt_2$$

$$+\beta_i^{-1}\beta_k^{-1}\Delta t \sum_l Q_l\bar{a}_{kl}[-1+\exp\ (V_l)]$$

$$\times \sum_j Q_j[\exp\ (V_j)] \int_t^{t+\Delta t} \eta_{ij}(t_1)\ dt_1$$

$$+\beta_i^{-1}\beta_k^{-1} \sum_{jl} Q_jQ_l \exp\ (V_j+V_l)$$

$$\times \int_t^{t+\Delta t} \int_t^{t+\Delta t} \eta_{ij}(t_1)\eta_{kl}(t_2)\,dt_1\,dt_2. \quad (6.7)$$

If one averages over the ensemble from which the a_{ij} are generated, then, in view of (6.5c), the middle two terms in (6.7) vanish and

$$\langle \Delta V_i \Delta V_k \rangle = (\Delta t)^2 \sum_{jl} Q_jQ_l\bar{a}_{ij}\bar{a}_{kl}$$

$$\times[-1+\exp\ (V_j)][-1+\exp\ (V_l)]\beta_i^{-1}\beta_k^{-1}$$

$$+\beta_i^{-1}\beta_k^{-1} \sum_{jl} Q_jQ_l \exp\ (V_j+V_l)$$

$$\times \int_t^{t+\Delta t} \int_t^{t+\Delta t} \langle \eta_{ij}(t_1)\eta_{kl}(t_2) \rangle dt_1\,dt_2. \quad (6.8)$$

The behavior of the second term in (6.8) depends on the character of the time correlations of variations of a_{ij} and a_{kl}, i.e., η_{ij} and η_{kl}. The remarks made above concerning the irrelevance of the dependence of the $V_i(t)$ on a_{ij} have been employed again in the derivation of (6.8).

We now derive a Fokker–Planck type of equation for $P(V^0, t_0\ |\ V, t)$, the probability that in time $t-t_0$, V varies from V^0 to V. The general form of the Fokker–Planck equation is

$$\partial P/\partial t = - \sum_i (\partial/\partial V_i)\{PA_i(V)\}$$

$$+\tfrac{1}{2}\sum_{ij} (\partial^2/\partial V_i\partial V_j)\{PB_{ij}(V)\}, \quad (6.9)$$

where

$$A_i(V) = \lim_{\Delta t \to 0} \langle \Delta V_i \rangle / \Delta t, \qquad (6.10a)$$

$$B_{ij}(V) = \lim_{\Delta t \to 0} \langle \Delta V_i \Delta V_j \rangle / \Delta t. \qquad (6.10b)$$

The appropriate averages are (6.6) and (6.8). $A_i(V)$ has been obtained explicitly and B_{ij} depends on the correlation functions appearing in (6.8).

One would expect the various rate constants to be independent of each other so that the time variation of their deviations from the mean would be uncorrelated. If the variation in rate constants is generated by a stationary random process, then correlations should depend only on $|t_1 - t_2|$ and we can write

$$\langle \eta_{ik}(t_1) \eta_{lj}(t_2) \rangle = (\delta_{il}\delta_{kj} - \delta_{ij}\delta_{kl}) F_{ik}(|t_1 - t_2|) \qquad (6.11a)$$

with

$$F_{ij}(t) = F_{ji}(t). \qquad (6.11b)$$

The Kronecker deltas ensure that the correlation vanishes unless $(i, k) \equiv (l, j)$ or (j, l) (since $\eta_{lj} = -\eta_{jl}$). In the classical theory of Brownian motion, one sets

$$F_{ik}(t) = \delta_{ik}\delta(t). \qquad (6.12)$$

This corresponds to the physical situation that is encountered when a large molecule or colloidal particle suffers many collisions with small molecules such that no correlations exist between individual collision with small molecules. An alternative form for $F_{ik}(t)$ would be one in which the driving force of the fluctuation persists for a while so that $F_{ik}(t)$ would change more slowly with time. That is, whatever causes the changes in dietary habits of species has a relaxation time which might persist over, say, $\frac{1}{2}$ to 5% of the lifetime of a member of a species.

We treat the latter case first for it is the one which

leads to the Kerner distribution. Consider the double integral in (6.8):

$$\int_t^{t+\Delta t} \int_t^{t+\Delta t} \langle \eta_{ij}(t_1) \eta_{kl}(t_2) \rangle dt_1 \, dt_2$$

$$= (\delta_{ij}\delta_{kl} - \delta_{il}\delta_{kj}) \int_t^{t+\Delta t} \int_t^{t+\Delta t} F_{ik}(t_1 - t_2) dt_1 \, dt_2$$

$$= (\delta_{ij}\delta_k - \delta_{il}\delta_{kj}) \int_t^{t+\Delta t} dt_1 \int_{t-t_2}^{t-t_2-\Delta t} F_{ik}(\tau) \, d\tau$$

$$\sim (\delta_{ij}\delta_{kl} - \delta_{il}\delta_{kj}) \Delta t \int_t^{t+\Delta t} F_{ik}(t-t_2) \, dt_2$$

$$\sim (\delta_{ij}\delta_{kl} - \delta_{il}\delta_{kj}) (\Delta t)^2 F_{ik}(0)$$

as $\Delta t \to 0$. Hence, if $F_{ik}(t)$ is not a delta function, but is more spread out, we have

$$\langle \Delta V_i \Delta V_k \rangle = O((\Delta t)^2) \tag{6.13}$$

and

$$B_{ij}(V) \to 0 \quad \text{as} \quad \Delta t \to 0.$$

On this basis, the second derivative terms in the Fokker–Planck equation (6.9) vanish, and when (6.6) is introduced, (6.9) becomes

$$\partial P/\partial t = \sum_{ij} (\partial/\partial V_i) \{ P Q_j \bar{a}_{ij} [-1 + \exp(V_j)] \} \beta_i^{-1}$$

$$= \sum_{ij} \bar{a}_{ij} Q_j \beta_i^{-1} [-1 + \exp(V_j)] (\partial P/\partial V_i). \tag{6.14}$$

Now let us seek the equilibrium distribution function, $p(V)$, by setting $\partial P/\partial t = 0$. Then $p(V)$ must satisfy

$$\sum_{i,k} \bar{a}_{ik} Q_k [-1 + \exp(V_k)] \beta_i^{-1} \partial p(V)/\partial V_i = 0. \tag{6.15}$$

A solution $p(V)$ which has a product form can be found. Let

$$p(V) \equiv \prod_j p_j(V_j). \tag{6.16}$$

Then we find

$$\partial p(V)/\partial V_i = p(V) d \log p_i(V_i)/dV_i \quad (6.17)$$

so that

$$p(V) \sum_{i,k} \beta_i^{-1} \bar{a}_{ik} Q_k [-1 + \exp (V_k)] d \log p_i(V_i)/dV_i = 0.$$

$$(6.18)$$

In view of the antisymmetry of the $\bar{a}_{ik}$, we see that if we set

$$d \log p_i(V_i)/dV_i = Q_i \beta_i [1 - \exp (V_i)]/I, \quad (6.19)$$

(where I is a constant yet to be determined), then (6.18) is satisfied.

The factor $p_i(V_i)$ is found by integrating (6.19)

$$p_i(V_i) = c_i \exp \{Q_i \beta_i [V_i - \exp (V_i)]/I\}, \quad (6.20a)$$

where c_i is an integration constant such that $p_i(V_i)$ is normalized. If we return to our basic variable N_i and choose c_i so that $p_i(N_i)$ is normalized according to

$$\int_0^\infty p_i(N_i) \, dN_i = 1, \quad (6.20b)$$

substitution of (6.20a) and the employment of (6.3) yield

$$p_i(V_i) = d_i \exp \{Q_i \beta_i [1 + V_i - \exp (V_i)]/I\} \quad (6.21a)$$

with

$$d_i^{-1} = \int_0^\infty \exp \{Q_i \beta_i [1 + V_i - \exp (V_i)]/I\} \, dN_i$$

$$= Q_i (eI/Q_i \beta_i)^{Q_i \beta_i/I} \Gamma (\beta_i Q_i/I), \quad (6.21b)$$

$\Gamma(x)$ being the classical gamma function. In terms of N_i, the distribution $p(N)$ has the Poisson form

$$p_i(N_i) = \left(\frac{\beta_i N_i}{I}\right)^{Q_i \beta_i / I} \frac{\exp\,(-\beta_i N_i / I)}{Q_i \Gamma(\beta_i Q_i / I)} \,. \quad (6.22)$$

The significance of the parameter I is obtained by calculating the mean value of the constant of the motion G_0 [see Eq. (1.9b)]:

$$\bar{G}_0 = -\left\langle \sum_j \beta_j Q_j [1 + V_j - \exp\,(V_j)] \right\rangle_{\mathrm{Av}}$$

$$= - \sum_i d_i \left(\frac{d}{d(I^{-1})}\right)$$

$$\times \int_0^\infty \exp\left(\frac{\alpha_j \beta_j [1 + V_j - \exp\,(V_j)]}{I}\right) dN_j$$

$$= - \sum_j d \log$$

$$\left\{\left[\int_0^\infty \exp\left(\frac{Q_j \beta_j (1 + V_j - \exp\,(V_j))}{I}\right) dN_j\right]\right\} / dI^{-1}$$

$$= - \sum_j d(\log d_j^{-1}) / dI^{-1}. \quad (6.23)$$

Then, from (6.21b), we have

$$\bar{G}_0 = - \sum_j Q_j \beta_j \left\{\log\left(\frac{I}{Q_j \beta_j}\right) + d \log \frac{\Gamma(Q_j \beta_j / I)}{d(Q_j \beta_j I^{-1})}\right\}. \quad (6.24)$$

When x is large, the Stirling approximation for $\Gamma(x)$ yields

$$d \log \Gamma(x) / dx = \log x - (1/2x) - (1/12x^2) \cdots.$$

If only the first two terms are retained in the expansion of the derivative of the gamma function in (6.24), the expression for $\bar{G}_0$ is

$$\bar{G}_0 \sim \sum_j \tfrac{1}{2} I \quad (6.25)$$

so that, as long as $Q_j \beta_j / I$ is large,

$$I \sim 2 \bar{G}_0 / n. \quad (6.26)$$

In the regime of small deviations from equilibrium [see (1.9b)], we have

$$2G_0/n \simeq n^{-1} \sum v_j^2 \beta_j q_j \simeq n^{-1} \sum_j (N_j - q_j)^2 \beta_j / q_j \quad (6.27)$$

which is essentially the mean square dispersion from equilibrium population.

The condition $Q_i \beta_i / I$ large is equivalent to

$$n^{-1} \sum_{j=1}^{n} \{ (N_j - Q_j)^2 \beta_j / \beta_i Q_i Q_j \} \text{ small}, \quad (6.28)$$

i.e., the mean relative deviation from equilibrium population is small compared with the equilibrium population.

Now consider the case which is analogous to classical Brownian motion in that we set

$$\langle \eta_{ij}(t_1) \eta_{kl}(t_2) \rangle = (\delta_{ik}\delta_{jl} - \delta_{il}\delta_{jk}) \sigma_{ij}^2 \delta(t_1 - t_2). \quad (6.29)$$

Then we have

$$\int_t^{t+\Delta t} \int_t^{t+\Delta t} \langle \eta_{ij}(t_1) \eta_{kl}(t_2) \rangle dt_1\, dt_2$$

$$= (\delta_{ik}\delta_{jl} - \delta_{il}\delta_{jk}) \sigma_{ij}^2 \int_t^{t+\Delta t} dt_2 \int_t^{t+\Delta t} \delta(t_1 - t_2)\, dt_1$$

$$= \Delta t \sigma_{ij}^2 (\delta_{ik}\delta_{jl} - \delta_{il}\delta_{jk}). \quad (6.30)$$

Hence, from (6.8), as $\Delta t \to 0$, we find

$$(\Delta t)^{-1} \langle \Delta V_i \Delta V_k \rangle = \beta_i^{-1} \beta^{-1} \{ -Q_k Q_i \sigma_{ik}^2$$
$$\times \exp (V_i + V_k) + \delta_{ik} \sum_j Q_j^2 \exp (2V_j) \sigma_{ij}^2 \}$$

$$= -\beta_i^{-1} \beta_k^{-1} Q_k Q_i \sigma_{ik}^2 \exp (V_i + V_k) \quad \text{if } i \neq k \quad (6.31a)$$

$$= \beta_i^{-2} \sum_{j \neq i} Q_j^2 \exp (2V_j) \sigma_{ij}^2 \quad \text{if } i = k. \quad (6.31b)$$

The Fokker–Planck equation for the probability distribution P follows from (6.9), (6.6), and (6.31). We have (prime implies that terms with $i=j$ are to be omitted)

$$\partial P/\partial t = - \sum_{ij} (\partial/\partial V_i) \{ P \beta_i^{-1} Q_j \bar{a}_{ij} [-1 + \exp (V_j)] \}$$

94

$$+\tfrac{1}{2} \sum_{ij}{}' \beta_i^{-1} Q_j^2 \sigma_{ij}{}^2 \frac{\partial^2 [\exp{(2V_j)}P]}{\partial V_i{}^2}$$

$$-\tfrac{1}{2} \sum_{ij}{}' \beta_i^{-1} \beta_j^{-1} Q_j Q_i \sigma_{ij}{}^2 (\partial^2/\partial V_i \partial V_j) \{P \exp{(V_i+V_j)}\}.$$

$$(6.32)$$

A product form for the stationary solution of this equation can be sought by setting $\partial P/\partial t = 0$ and postulating that $P(V_1, \cdots, V_n) = \prod p_j(V_j) \equiv \prod p_j$. One finds that

$$0 = \sum_{ij}{}' \left\{ \beta_i^{-1} Q_j \bar{a}_{ij} [1 - \exp{(V_j)}] \frac{d \log p_i}{dV_i} \right.$$

$$+ \tfrac{1}{2} \beta_i^{-1} Q_j^2 \sigma_{ij}{}^2 \exp{(2V_j)} p_i^{-1} \frac{d^2 p_i}{dV_i{}^2}$$

$$+ \tfrac{1}{2} \beta_i^{-1} \beta_j^{-1} Q_i Q_j \sigma_{ij}{}^2 (p_i p_j)^{-1}$$

$$\left. \times \left[\frac{d[p_i \exp{(V_i)}]}{dV_i} \right] \left[\frac{d[p_j \exp{(V_j)}]}{dV_j} \right] \right\}. \quad (6.33)$$

If the population N_j is to have the Poisson distribution (6.22), then V_j has the distribution whose derivative is given by (6.19):

$$d \log p_j/dV_j = Q_j \beta_j [1 - \exp{(V_j)}] \alpha,$$

where α is a constant. If this is substituted into (6.33), the first term vanishes. However, the remaining combination does not, even if $\sigma_{ij}{}^2$ has a product form, say $\sigma_{ij}{}^2 = (\text{const})/Q_i Q_j$. Hence the equilibrium distribution function does not have a product form.

In conclusion, if the "rate constants" are considered to be random variables, the stationary population distribution is Poisson if the variation in the "rate constants" is not too rapid. If the variation has an autocorrelation function of a delta function form as postulated in the classical theory of Brownian motion, then the equilibrium distribution is not Poisson.

Interacting but Lets die

VIII. Population Growth as Birth and Death Processes

In this section we will briefly discuss another stochastic model for the population growth of interacting and competing species. In this model, which originally is due to Chiang (1954), the number of individuals of the various species are taken to be random variables and a differential equation for the probability distribution of these variables having certain values is derived in terms of probabilities of birth and death of the individuals. The probability distribution can then be used to calculate the average population.

Let us consider a two-species (S_1 and S_2) system and let $X(t)$ and $Y(t)$ be the random variables which denote the population sizes of the two species. Let $P(x, y; t)$, $x, y = 0, 1, \cdots$ be the joint probability distribution function for $X(t)$ being x and $Y(t)$ being y. The events which can cause a change in the population sizes of the two species and, hence, in $P(x, y; t)$, are as follows:

(a) Birth of one individual of species S_1 during the time interval $(t, t+\Delta t)$. Let the probability of this event be $p_x \Delta t + O(\Delta t)$.

(b) Death of one individual of species S_1 during the time interval $(t, t+\Delta t)$. Let the probability of this event be $q_x \Delta t + O(\Delta t)$.

(c) and (d) Events corresponding to (a) and (b) but for the species S_2. Let the corresponding probabilities be $p_y \Delta t + O(\Delta t)$ and $q_y \Delta t + O(\Delta t)$, respectively. The p's and q's depend on the interaction between the species.

Let us also assume that the probability of a change of

absolute value greater than one in the number of individuals of S_1 and S_2 in the interval $(t, t+\Delta t)$ is $O(\Delta t)$. It is now easy to see that $P(x, y; t)$ satisfies the differential equation

$$dP(x, y; t)/dt = -(p_x+q_x+p_y+q_y)P(x, y; t)$$
$$+p_{x-1}P(x-1, y; t)+P_{y-1}(x, y-1; t)$$
$$+q_{x+1}P(x+1, y; t)+q_{y+1}P(x, y+1; t). \quad (7.1)$$

Since negative population is unphysical, we have

$$P(x, y; t) = 0 \qquad x < 0 \quad \text{or} \quad y < 0 \quad \text{or} \quad x, y < 0 \quad (7.2)$$

The solution of (7.1) depends on the type of interaction. Let us consider the case of prey–predator interaction: Let S_1 be the prey and S_2 be the predator. In analogy with the deterministic case, we make the following assumptions for the coefficients p and q of (7.1):

$$p_x = \alpha_1 x, \qquad q_x = \lambda_1 xy,$$
$$p_y = \lambda_2 xy, \qquad q_y = \alpha_2 y. \quad (7.3)$$

Substituting (7.3) into (7.1), we obtain a differential equation which can, in principle, be solved. The standard method for solving (7.3) is to introduce a generating function defined by

$$G(s, z; t) = \sum_{x=0}^{\infty} \sum_{y=0}^{\infty} s^x z^y P(x, y; t). \quad (7.4)$$

Multiplying (7.1) by $s^x z^y$ and summing over x and y, we get the differential equation satisfied by $G(s, z, t)$, i.e.,

$$\partial G/\partial t = \alpha_1 s(s-1)(\partial G/\partial s) - \alpha_2(z-1)(\partial G/\partial z)$$
$$+[\lambda_2 z(1-s)+\lambda_1 sz(z-1)](\partial^2 G/\partial z \partial s). \quad (7.5)$$

P is the coefficient of $s^x z^y$ in the expansion of G. Without solving (7.5) for G, some insight into the model can be gained by studying the equations for the moments of

x and y. Let $E(x)$ and $E(y)$ denote the expectation value of x and y, i.e.,

$$E(x) = \sum_{0}^{\infty} \sum_{0}^{\infty} xP(x, y; t), \qquad (7.6\text{a})$$

$$E(y) = \sum_{0}^{\infty} \sum_{0}^{\infty} yP(x, y; t); \qquad (7.6\text{b})$$

from (7.1) and (7.3)

$$dE(x)/dt = \alpha_1 E(x) - \lambda_1 E(xy), \qquad (7.7\text{a})$$

$$dE(y)/dt = -\alpha_2 E(y) + \lambda_2 E(xy). \qquad (7.7\text{b})$$

These equations are to be compared with the deterministic equations (1.1). $E(x)$ and $E(y)$ are the analogs of N_1 and N_2. Owing to the fact that one species feeds on the other, the population sizes of S_1 and S_2 are mutually dependent. Hence

$$E(xy) \neq E(x)E(y).$$

Therefore, this stochastic model is different from the deterministic one.

There are several ways in which this process can be discussed systematically. One is to solve Eq. (7.5) and then calculate the various expectation values $E(x)$, $E(y)$, $E(xy)$, etc. Another is to construct a hierarchy of equations for expectation values of x, y, xy, x^2, y^2, x^3, etc. Equations (7.7) are the first in such a hierarchy. A first approximation to the solution would be found by making the independence approximation $E(xy) = E(x)E(y)$, which would yield the Volterra equations. A second approximation might correspond to writing

$$E(xy) = E(x)E(y) + [E(xy) - E(x)E(y)]$$

and treating the term in the bracket as a random driving force. Higher approximations would involve truncation of the hierarchy at a higher level.

Lefever, Nicolis, and Prigogine (1967) (see, also, Nicolis, 1970) have been conducting a systematic investigation of processes of this form.

IX. Time Lags in Population

In the preceding sections we have been assuming that the members of the population can react instantaneously to any change in the environment and that the prey–predator interactions instantaneously affect the population of both the prey and the predator. Further, we have been assuming that all the members of the species survive to the same age, and the egg is instantaneously converted into an adult. In other words, we assume that all the members of a species have the same age. In this section we will make some remarks about the population when these assumptions are relaxed.

We shall first consider the single-species case. One model which partly takes into account the effect of age distribution is governed by the equation

$$dN(t)/dt = k[1 - (1/\theta)N(t-\tau)]N(t), \qquad \tau > 0. \quad (8.1)$$

In this model it is assumed that the birth rate coefficient is diminished by a quantity proportional to the population of the preceding generation, τ being the generation time (the time required in going from an egg stage to the adult stage). Equation (8.1), which is an ordinary difference-differential equation, has been investigated by several investigators (Cunningham, 1955; Wright, 1955; Kakutani and Markus, 1958; Jones, 1961). In particular, they studied the stability of the solution for various values of τ and other parameters. In other words, for what range of values of the parameter, does $N(t)$ oscillate, asymptotically approach zero, or asymptotically go to infinity? We will give only some of the results without derivation.

Let us rewrite (8.1) as

$$dz(t)/dt = [a - z(t-1)]z(t), \qquad (8.2)$$

101

where

$$z(t) = (k/\theta)\tau N(t\tau),\qquad\qquad (8.3a)$$

$$a = k\tau.\qquad\qquad (8.3b)$$

The steady state solution of Eq. (8.2) is

$$z(t) = a.\qquad\qquad (8.4)$$

Let $\phi(t)$, $0 \le t \le 1$, be a continuous real-valued function representing the initial condition $[z(t) = \phi(t), 0 \le t \le 1]$. In addition to proving theorems about the existence and uniqueness of the solution, Kakutani and Markus (1958) prove the following theorem:

(1) The intersections of the solution curve $z = z(t)$ with the line $z = a$ are discrete on $0 \le t < \infty$ if there are a finite number of zeros of $\phi(t) - a$ on $0 \le t \le 1$.

The following theorems are true only for $a > 0$, $\phi(1) > 0$:

(2) $0 < m \le z(t) \le M < \infty$, $1 \le t < \infty$, where

$$M = \max\{\max_{1 \le t \le 3} z(t), ae^a\},$$

$$m = \min\{\min_{1 \le t \le 3} z(t), ae^{a-M}\}.\qquad (8.5)$$

(3) Either $z(t)$ is asymptotic to $z = a$, i.e.,

$$\lim_{t\to\infty} z(t) = a,\qquad \lim_{t\to\infty} z'(t) = 0\qquad (8.6)$$

or $z(t)$ oscillates about $z = a$. For sufficiently large t, each zero of $z(t) - a$ is simple and there is exactly one zero of $z'(t)$ between consecutive zeros of $z(t) - a$.

(4) For $a \le 1$, if $z(t) - a$ oscillates with discrete zeros, then the oscillations are damped and $\lim_{t\to\infty} z(t) = a$.

(5) For $a > 1/e$, no solution $z(t)$ is asymptotic to $z = a$ (except $z(t) \equiv a$).

(6) From Theorems (4) and (5), therefore, if $1/e < a \le 1$, then every solution is a damped solution tending to the limit value of a.

(7) For $a \le 1/e$, let the interval between the zeros of $z(t) - a$ be at least one for large t. Then the solution $z(t)$ is asymptotic to $z = a$.

102

There are other theorems for $a \leq 0$ and $\phi(1) \leq 0$, but they are more of mathematical interest than of practical usefulness. An additional theorem was given by Jones (1961). According to this theorem, for all $a > \frac{1}{2}\pi$, there exist nonconstant periodic solutions. Jones (1961) also computes numerically the periodic forms. Dunkel (1968) generalizes (8.1) to the equation

$$\dot{N}(t) = \left[k + \int_{\tau}^{T} \psi(N(t-a)) \, ds(a) \right] N(t). \quad (8.7)$$

This equation represents the population growth for which k is the constant birth rate, $s(a)$ is the fraction of N surviving to age a, T is the maximum life span, and τ is the time it takes for an increase in population to increase the death rate, and ψ measures how much an increase in N increases the death rate. Let the equation

$$\psi(N) = k/s(\tau) \quad (8.8)$$

have a unique and positive solution N^*. Then Dunkel (1968) shows that for (8.7), the following are true:

(1) All solutions are uniformly bounded and

$$0 < N(t) \leq \max \{N(0); N^* e^{kT}\}. \quad (8.9)$$

(2) If $k\tau > 1$ and $\psi(N^*) = \alpha N^*$, α a constant, then, if $\psi(N) \leq \alpha N$, no nontrivial solution is forever increasing and, if $\psi(N) \geq \alpha N$, no nontrivial solution is forever decreasing.

(3) As a corollary of (2), if $\psi(N) \leq kN (N \leq N^*)$, and $\psi(N) \geq kN (N \geq N^*)$, then all solutions oscillate.

(4) Let $\psi(N^*) = \alpha N^*$. If $\psi(N) \geq kN (N \leq N^*)$, $\psi(N) \leq kN (N \geq N^*)$, and $kT \leq 1$, then we have

$$N(t) \rightarrow N^* \quad \text{as} \quad t \rightarrow \infty. \quad (8.10)$$

(5) For $\tau > 0$, k sufficiently large, and if $\psi(N) \leq kN (N \leq N^*)$, $\psi(N) \geq kN (N \geq N^*)$, then there exists a periodic solution.

Levin (1965, 1969) further generalizes (8.7) by taking k to be time dependent and finds the conditions under which the solution is oscillatory, asymptotically stable, etc.

Since the study of the stability of the nonlinear equation is rather involved and difficult, it is desirable to know whether any conclusions can be made about the solutions of the nonlinear equations by studying their linearized forms.

As an example, let us consider (8.2). Substituting $z=a+u$ into (8.2) and keeping only linear terms, we find

$$du/dt = -au(t-1). \qquad (8.11a)$$

Making the substitution

$$u = Ae^{\lambda t} \qquad (8.12)$$

into (8.11a), we have

$$\lambda e^{\lambda} + a = 0. \qquad (8.13)$$

The roots of this equation were derived by Wright (1959; see also Appendix D). One finds that

$$\text{Re } (\lambda) < 0 \quad \text{if} \quad 0 < a < \pi/2. \qquad (8.14)$$

Therefore, we have $N(t) \to 0$ as $t \to \infty$ provided (8.14) is satisfied, which, as mentioned earlier in the section, is also true for the nonlinear case. In fact, there exists such a theorem (Bellman and Cooke, 1963; see also Pinney, 1958, and Halanay, 1966) which is applicable for small perturbations from the steady state values for the population (all time derivatives$=0$). According to this theorem (Theorem 11.2, Bellman and Cooke, 1963), any solutions of

$$a_0[du(t)/dt] + b_0u(t) + b_1u(t-\tau)$$
$$= f[u(t), u(t-\tau)], \qquad t > \tau, \quad (8.15)$$

with initial condition

$$u(t) = g(t), \qquad 0 < t < \tau,$$

with g and f having the properties,

$$\max_{0 \le t \le \tau} | g(t) |$$

sufficiently small and $f(u, v)$ a continuous function of u and v in a neighborhood of origin $|u| + |v| \leq c_1$ and

$$\lim_{|u|+|v|\to 0} |f(u, v)|/(|u| + |v|) = 0,$$

can be continued over the interval $0 \leq t < \infty$ and each such solution satisfies

$$\lim_{t\to\infty} |u(t)| \to 0$$

provided *every* continuous solution of the linear equation

$$a_0[du(t)/dt] + b_0 u(t) + b_1 u(t-\tau) = 0 \qquad (8.16)$$

goes to zero as $t \to \infty$.

In other words, if all the solutions of linear equation$\to 0$ as $t \to \infty$, i.e., Re $(\lambda) < 0$ (λ being any of the roots of the characteristic equation) for all λ, then all the solutions of nonlinear equations will have the same asymptotic behavior. This theorem can be extended to set of equations in many variables.

We may further ask the question whether any conclusions can be made about the solution of the linear or nonlinear equation by making Taylor's expansion in τ and keeping terms up to a certain order in τ. This procedure in effect enables one to approximate an infinite order differential equation by one of finite order. This procedure is an invalid one and the results obtained may give wrong conclusions about the exact linear or nonlinear equation. As an example of a linear equation, let us consider

$$du/dt = -au(t-\tau) \qquad (8.11b)$$

and find for small τ, for which values of a, $N(t) \to 0$ as $t \to \infty$. Expanding the right-hand side of (8.11b) in a Taylor's series and keeping terms linear in τ, we get

$$dN/dt + [a/(1-a\tau)]N = 0. \qquad (8.17)$$

Therefore, we have $N(t) \to 0$ as $t \to \infty$ if and only if,

$$a(1-a\tau)^{-1} < 0, \quad \text{i.e.,} \quad 0 < a < 1/\tau, \qquad (8.18)$$

105

a condition which differs from the exact condition

$$0 < a < \pi/2\tau. \qquad (8.19)$$

This latter condition is obtained by the method similar to that used for obtaining the condition (8.14).

As an example of nonlinear equation, let us consider (8.1). Expand $N(t-\tau)$ in powers of τ keeping terms only up to d^2N/dt^2. This procedure has been followed by Cunningham (1954). He studied the resulting equation and found that the sustained oscillations occurred when $k\tau \geq 1.0$, which is different from the exact result $k\tau > \pi/2$ obtained by Jones (1961) and, also, by Cunningham (1954) by numerical solution of (8.1).

A more dramatic example is the prey–predator population model with time lag studied by Wangersky and Cunningham (1957). In the model they use, the population is governed by the equations

$$dN_1/dt = k_1 N_1(t)[\theta - N_1(t)]/\theta + a_{12} N_1(t) N_2(t), \quad (8.20a)$$

$$dN_2/dt = k_2 N_2(t) + a_{21} N_1(t-\tau) N_2(t-\tau), \qquad (8.20b)$$

i.e., the change in the number of predators (N_2) depends on the number of preys (N_1) and predators present at some previous time. In (8.20a) and (8.20b), we have $k_1 > 0$, $k_2 < 0$, $a_{12} < 0$, $a_{21} > 0$. On linearizing the equations around the equilibrium point, we find

$$q_1 = -k_2/a_2, \qquad q_2 = k_1[1 - q_1\theta^{-1}]a_{12}, \qquad (8.21)$$

i.e., substituting

$$N_1(t) = q_1 + y_1(t), \qquad N_2(t) = q_2 + y_2(t) \qquad (8.22)$$

into (8.20a) and (8.20b), retaining only linear terms, and eliminating y_2, we obtain

$$y_1'' + (A+C)y_1'(p) - Ay_1'(p) + ACy_1(p)$$
$$+ A(B-C)y_1(p-1) = 0, \quad (8.23)$$

where

$$p = t/\tau, \ y_1' \equiv dy_1/dp, \qquad (8.24a)$$

$$A = -k_2\tau > 0, \qquad (8.24b)$$

106

$$B = -a_{12}q_3\tau > 0, \qquad (8.24c)$$

$$C = B/(z-1), \, z = \theta/q_1. \qquad (8.24d)$$

Substituting

$$y_1(p) = e^{\lambda t} \qquad (8.25)$$

into (8.23), we have

$$e^\lambda[\lambda^2 + (A+C)\lambda + AC] - A\lambda + A(B-C) = 0. \quad (8.26)$$

To determine the roots of this equation it is convenient to make the substitution

$$\lambda' = \lambda - (B-C). \qquad (8.27)$$

Equation (8.26) then becomes

$$e^{\lambda'}[\lambda'^2 + (A+2B-C)\lambda' + B(A+B-C)] - Ae^{C-B}\lambda' = 0.$$
$$(8.28)$$

The roots of this equation have been investigated in the literature (Bellman and Cooke, 1963). According to Theorem 13.10 of Bellman and Cooke (1963), all the roots of (8.28) will have real part less than 0 if and only if,

$$1 - Ae^{C-B}(A+2B-C)^{-1} \cos a_\omega > 0 \qquad (8.29)$$

provided

$$A+2B-C > 0, \qquad (8.30)$$

$$A+B-C \geq 0, \qquad (8.31)$$

and $a_k(k \geq 0)$ is the sole root of the equation

$$\tan a = [B(A+B-C) - a^2]/(A+2B-C)a \quad (8.32)$$

which lies on the interval $(k\pi - \pi/2, \, k\pi + \pi/2)$, and ω is the even k for which a_k lies closest to $\{B(A+B-C)\}^{1/2}$.

If $|-Ae^{C-B}/(A+2B-C)| < 1$, (8.29) is always true and this implies Re $\lambda' < 0$. From (8.30), (8.31), and (8.27), we see that

$$\text{Re } \lambda < 0 \qquad (8.33)$$

if

$$B < C < A + B \qquad (8.34a)$$

and

$$A e^{C-B} / (A + 2B - C) < 1. \qquad (8.34b)$$

Substituting the upper limit of C from (8.34a) into (8.34b), we have

$$A e^A < B. \qquad (8.34c)$$

Thus, if (8.34a) and (8.34c) are satisfied, the population will be asymptotically stable (even for the nonlinear case, according to the theorem stated earlier in the section).

Let us now compare the above results with the corresponding results obtained by Wangersky and Cunningham (1957) by expanding (8.23) in a Taylor series and retaining terms up to second derivatives of y_1. The equation thus obtained is

$$[1 + A + A(B-C)/2]y_1''$$
$$+ [C - A(B-C)]y_1' + ABy_1 = 0. \qquad (8.35)$$

Substituting

$$y_1 = \exp[(\alpha + i\beta)p], \qquad (8.36)$$

we find that

$$\alpha = \frac{1}{2} \frac{A(B-C) - C}{1 + A + (A/2)(B-C)} \qquad (8.37)$$

and $\beta^2 > 0$ if $z > z_c$, where

$$z_c = 1 + \frac{-A + [A^2 + (1+A)^2(4A/B + 4A^2/B + A^2)]^{1/2}}{(4A/B + 4A^2/B + A^2)}.$$

$$(8.38)$$

From (8.36), we have $y_1(t) \to 0$ as $t \to \infty$ if $\alpha < 0$, i.e., from (8.36), if

$$[A/(1+A)]B < C < 2(1 + 1/A) + B. \qquad (8.39)$$

The lower limit obtained without expanding into a Taylor series [Eq. (8.34a)] is higher than the lower limit obtained by using the Taylor's expansion [Eq. (8.39)]. However, if A and B are large enough and still (8.34c) is satisfied, then the upper end of the region of asymptotic stability as given by (8.34a) could be significantly larger than that given by (8.39).

We now make a few remarks about the population of several interacting species which grows according to conditions some time earlier. Let the dynamics of the population be described by the equations

$$dN_i/dt = k_i N_i(t) + (1/\beta_i) \sum_j a_{ij} N_i(t) N_j(t-\tau). \quad (8.40)$$

We first show that G, as defined by (1.9a), is not a constant of this system. From (8.40) we have

$$\beta_i \dot{v}_i(t) = \sum_j a_{ij} q_j \{\exp [v_j(t-\tau)] - 1\}, \quad v_i = \ln (N_i/q_i), \quad (8.41)$$

where q_i is the steady state value of N_i. Therefore, we find

$$dG/dt = (d/dt) \sum_i \beta_i q_i [\exp (v_i) - v_i]$$

$$= \sum_{ij} a_{ij} q_i q_j \{\exp [v_j(t-\tau)] - 1\} \{\exp [v_i(t)] - 1\} \neq 0 \quad (8.42)$$

which proves the assertion that G is not a constant of motion. We have been unable[3] to find any other constant of motion for the system described by (8.40). In the absence of a constant of motion, the applicability of methods of statistical mechanics is questionable.

We will now show that in the limit of small deviations from the stationary values of the populations of various systems, N_i increases exponentially, independ-

---

[3] However, Dr. P. Nowasad has pointed out that if det $a_{ij} = 0$ and $\Sigma_i a_{ij} c_i = 0$, $\Sigma_i k_i \beta_i c_i = 0$, then from (1.2), $\Pi_i N_i^{c_i}$ is a constant of motion even with the time lag. These two conditions involving c_i are the necessary conditions for the existence of q_i's.

ent of the magnitude of τ. In this limit, (8.40) becomes

$$\dot{x}_i(t) = \sum_j C_{ij}x_j(t-\tau), \qquad (8.43)$$

where C_{ij} is defined by (4.4). Let

$$x_i(t) = A_i e^{\lambda t} \qquad (8.44)$$

be the solution of (8.43). Substituting (8.44) into (8.43), we find

$$\sum C_{ij}A_j = \lambda e^{\lambda \tau}A_i. \qquad (8.45)$$

Comparing this equation with (4.6) we have

$$\lambda e^{\lambda \tau} = i\omega, \qquad (8.46)$$

where $i\omega$ is the eigenvalue of the matrix C. As shown in the Appendix D, for any value of τ, however small, the real parts of all the roots of the above equation are **not** negative and, therefore, x_i does not go to the limit 0 **as** $t \to \infty$. Therefore, from the theorem mentioned earlier in the section, there are no values of τ for which $N_i \to 0$ as $t \to \infty$. We cannot say on the basis of analysis of the linear equations whether N_i will oscillate or $\to \infty$ as $t \to \infty$.

Let us now investigate the effects of the Verhulst terms and determine whether the solution is asymptotically stable and, if so, for what values of the parameters. The dynamics of the population is assumed to be described by

$$\dot{N}_i = [k_i + \sum_j a_{ij}N_j(t-\tau)]N_i(t), \qquad a_{ii}<0. \quad (8.47)$$

Substituting

$$N_i = q_i + y_i, \qquad (8.48)$$

where q_i are the equilibrium values, and linearizing the equation, we find

$$\dot{x}_i(t) = \sum_j C_{ij}x_j(t-\tau), \qquad (8.49)$$

where C_{ij} is given by (4.4) and

$$C_{ii} = a_{ii}q_i = -\beta_i, \qquad \beta_i>0. \qquad (8.50)$$

Let

$$x_i = A_i e^{\lambda t} \qquad (8.51)$$

be the solution of (8.49). Substituting (8.51) into (8.49), we have

$$\sum C_{ij} A_j = A_i (\lambda e^{\lambda \tau} + \beta_i). \qquad (8.52)$$

The characteristic equation is

$$\det \left[(\lambda e^{\lambda \tau} + \beta_i) \delta_{ij} - C_{ij} \right] = 0. \qquad (8.53)$$

This algebraic equation can be written as

$$\prod_n (\lambda e^{\lambda \tau} + \gamma_n) = 0, \qquad (8.54)$$

where $-\gamma_1, -\gamma_2, \cdots, -\gamma_n$ are the roots of the algebraic Eq. (8.53). Therefore, the sufficient condition for $N_i \to q_i$ as $t \to \infty$ [see Appendix D] is

$$\pi/2 - |\theta_n| < \rho_n, \quad \text{for all } n, \quad \gamma_n = \rho_n \exp(i\theta_n). \qquad (8.55)$$

This follows from an extension of the theorem given earlier (Bellman and Cooke, 1963) for many-variable systems.

We conclude this section by mentioning another model for single-species growth which is slightly different than the one studied by Kakutani and Marcus (1958) which has been numerically investigated (Smith, 1969). In this model the population is governed by

$$dN(t)/dt = k[1 - \theta^{-1} N(t-\tau)] N(t-\tau) - k'N(t).$$

In other words, though it is assumed that the growth in population is proportional to the preceding generation, the death rate at any instant is proportional to the instantaneous value of the population.

X. Generalization of Volterra Equations

We had noted in the Introduction that Volterra's model for the population of interacting species does not include some features about the population. Among these features, we have already pointed out population-dependent rate constants (Verhulst term), members of the population of a particular species having different ages, time lags in the reaction of the members of the population to any change in the environment, and interaction with members of the population of other species. We have also briefly investigated the change in the behavior of the population when these effects are included. We will now briefly mention some of the work done in recent years in an attempt to generalize and to modify the Volterra equations. These generalizations serve at least two purposes. First they throw some light on the behavior of the population if the model is changed, and, second, the generalized equations may be more realistic in describing the behavior of other systems of interacting species.

The generalized equations have been studied, both analytically and numerically.

Gause and Witt (1935) studied analytically Volterra's equation with Verhulst terms for a two-species system and showed that the theory of growth of mixed populations of two species is directly connected with the problem of natural selection. They also showed that, under the action of a temperature (or any other) gradient, mixed populations separate into a number of distinct types. Further discussion of these same equations can be found in the books by Kostitzin (1939) and Slobodkin (1961). Hutchinson (1947) also studied the Volterra's equation with Verhulst term, except that the prey–predator interaction term is taken to be ternary instead of binary, i.e., the prey–predator system is modeled by the equations

$$dN_1/dt = \alpha_1 N_1 (k_1 - N_1 - m_1 N_2^2), \qquad (9.1a)$$

$$dN_2/dt = \alpha_2 N_2 (k_2 - N_2 - m_2 N_1^2). \qquad (9.1b)$$

Cunningham (1955) generalized the equations studied by Hutchinson (1947) to

$$dN_1/dt = \alpha_1 N_1 [k_1 - N_1 - F_1(N_2)], \qquad (9.2a)$$

$$dN_2/dt = \alpha_2 N_2 [k_2 - N_2 - F_2(N_1)]. \qquad (9.2b)$$

However, he did not find a general condition for the existence of periodic solutions. Some solutions were also found using an analog computer. Utz and Waltman (1963) found the sufficient conditions for the existence of periodic solutions for the equations studied by Cunningham. In addition, they also studied the equations

$$dN_1/dt = N_1 F_1(N_2), \qquad (9.3a)$$

$$dN_2/dt = N_2 F_2(N_1) \qquad (9.3b)$$

and found the sufficient conditions for the existence of periodic solutions, but these conditions do not describe a prey–predator situation. Equations (9.3a) and (9.3b) also occur in the theory of war (Richardson, 1960). Waltman (1964) generalized these equations further to

$$dN_i/dt = N_i K_i(N_1, N_2), \qquad i = 1, 2, \qquad (9.4)$$

and found conditions for the periodic solutions using a certain bifurcation theorem. Rescigno and Richardson (1967) further studied Waltmann's equation (9.4) for various functions K_i's. Later on, the study was generalized to the three-species case (Rescigno, 1968).

In addition to analytical work, some numerical work has been done on the two-and-three-species system. Garfinkel (1962) considers the system of two and three species, grass (prey) and rabbits (predator), and grass, rabbits, and foxes (predator for rabbits), and does numerical computations for various values of the efficiencies with which the predators attack their appropriate preys. This work and some aspects of the method are reviewed in Garfinkel (1965). The studies were extended (Garfinkel, 1967a) to eight ecological systems, consisting of up to 10 species, belonging to the trophic levels of plant, herbivore, carnivore, and supercarnivore. It was shown that the Verhulst terms tend to stabilize the system, but the extent depends on the trophic levels of the species for which the Verhulst term is nonzero; the lower the trophic level, the more the stabilization. Five of these eight ecosystems were studied further (Garfinkel, 1967b) to determine the effect of imposing strict territorial limits. It was shown that setting a territorial limit on the population of a species stabilizes the system, the stability being maximum for the herbivorous species. It may be noted that the growth rate of the population of a species in which the Verhulst term is introduced decreases continuously as its population increases, while, in the present case of territorial limits, population increases equally easily until it is sufficient to occupy the last vacant territory, but not at all thereafter. Pennycuick *et al.* (1968) describe a computer program which simulates the growth of a population of two species divided into age groups and which allows fecundity and survival density dependence. King and Paulik (1967) describe a computer program for single-species growth which is very flexible in the sense of incorporating the fine features of the growing population.

To assist in determining the accuracy of Volterra's model for the two-species system, Bellman *et al.* (1966) gave a method (based on the technique of quasi-linearization) of computing the six parameters $N_1(0)$, $N_2(0)$, k_1, k_2, a_{12}, and a_{21} of the Volterra model for a given set of values of $N_1(t)$, $N_2(t)$ at a set of time intervals.

A large number of models for oscillating chemical reactions have been studied on an analog computer by

115

Higgins (1967). These models, which are similar to the Lotka model for autocatalytic reactions, can easily be adapted to the study of population of interacting biological species.

The work on the generalization of the many-species Volterra's model is not as extensive as that for the few species, in particular, two-and-three-species system. Analytical study of any generalized model is difficult and the numerical study is expensive. The only study which has been made is the statistical mechanical study of those equations which are equivalent to the Volterra's equation. One set of such equations is

$$dU_i/dt = (m_i k_i) U_i - (m_i a_{ii}) U_i^{1/m_i+1}$$
$$+ (m_i/\beta_i) \sum_j a_{ij} U_i U_j^{1/m_j} \quad (9.5)$$

which can be transformed into the Volterra's equations with Verhulst terms by making the transformation

$$U_i = N_i^{m_i}.$$

Equation (9.5) can represent the population of interacting biological species with a population-dependent growth rate constant and prey–predator interactions different from the one we studied in this paper.

Another set of equations is

$$dN_i/dT = (k_i + \beta_i^{-1} \sum_{j=1}^{n} a_{ij} N_j) N_i (1 - N_i); \quad i = 1, 2, \cdots,$$
$$(9.6)$$

or

$$d \log N_i (1 - N_i)^{-1}/dT = k_i + \beta_i^{-1} \sum_j a_{ij} N_j. \quad (9.7)$$

These equations admit

$$G = \sum_i \beta_i \{ \ln [1 + q_i \exp (V_i)] - q_i V_i \}; \quad V_i = \log N_i/q_i,$$
$$(9.8)$$

as the constant of motion and can be studied using statistical mechanical methods described earlier in this paper. Equations (9.6) were derived by Cowan (1968) to represent the change in the nervous activity in the central nervous system arising from the interactions within and between assemblies of nervous nets. n is the number of neurons and N_i is a dynamic variable measuring the sensitivity of the ith neuron in a net. It measures the fraction of time in a long-time interval during which the neuron is not refractory, i.e., the fraction of time in which it can be fired. T is a dimensionless variable and is in seconds τ^{-1}, where τ is the mean intercellular transmittal time for neural activity from a certain point of one cell (say the end where the impulse enters) to the same point of the neighboring cells, the mean being taken over all the neighboring cells. k_i is a "growth coefficient" and is a function of the various electrical parameters of the neural membrane, as is β_i. In general, k_i may also depend on stimuli. The nature of the coupling coefficients a_{ij} depends on whether the synapse between ith and jth cells is excitatory or inhibitory. Cowan performs the statistical mechanical analysis similar to the one described in this paper and cites experimental data to support the model for the nervous system. In obtaining (9.6), Cowan makes several assumptions and among them is the one involving going from finite difference to differential equations. A critical analysis of various dynamical theories of nervous systems is under preparation and will be communicated in the future.

Another system which has been subjected to the same statistical mechanical analysis is a system of interacting biochemical metabolic oscillators (Goodwin, 1963). The oscillator is schematically shown in Fig. 9. L_i represents the genetic locus (on the DNA molecule) which synthesizes mRNA in quantities represented by the variable X_i. R is the cellular structure (a ribosome) where the information carried by mRNA is used in the synthesis of a particular species of protein in quantities denoted by the variable Y_i. C is a cellular locus where the protein influences (e.g., by enzyme action) the generation of the metabolic species in quantity M_i.

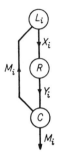

FIG. 9. Biochemical metabolic oscillator.

If M_i exceeds some preassigned value, the excess interacts with the genetic locus and represses the activity of L_i, i.e., synthesis of mRNA. By making several assumptions, the control equations for protein synthesis are simplified to

$$dX_i/dt = a_i/(A_i + k_i Y_i) - b_i, \qquad (9.9a)$$

$$dY_i/dt = \alpha_i X_i - \beta_i, \qquad (9.9b)$$

where a_i, b_i, A_i, k_i, α_i, and β_i are constants. These equations admit a constant of motion

$$G = \alpha_i (X_i^2/2) - \beta_i X_i + b_i Y_i - (a_i/k_i) \ln (A_i + k_i Y_i),$$

$$(9.10)$$

and, therefore, a plot of X_i vs Y_i is a closed curve and both $X_i(t)$ and $Y_i(t)$ are periodic. Various oscillators can be coupled through feedback of the metabolite of an oscillator to not only its own genetic locus, but also to the genetic loci of several other oscillators. It may be pointed out that Eqs. (9.9) are obtained by making several simplifying assumptions, some of which are probably not quite justified. Goodwin (1963) carries out in detail a statistical mechanical treatment of the system in which each oscillator is coupled to two "nearest neighbor" oscillators. The time lag in this system corresponds to the time for the diffusion of a metabolite from the location where it is made to the genetic loci. This time is assumed to be zero in Goodwin's analysis. Woolley and DeRocco (1970) have generalized the statistical mechanical analysis of systems of biochemical oscillators to arbitrary strong coupling and for arbitrary parallel coupling of metabolic pools and genetic loci.

Recently Woolley (1970) has used Goodwin's model for the bacterial growth cycle. It is very common in bacterial growth that the generation time changes if the environments (culturing medium) are changed appropriately, but the generation time changes to the original value if the environments are changed back. Woolley (1970) has given a set of five equations [two coupled equations like Goodwin's equation (1963) for the biochemical oscillator which represent a highly protected circuit, two coupled equations which represent a hemeostat which responds to the perturbation, and an equation which couples the two systems—the highly protected system and the control system], without any biochemical justification of the equations for the control system. He shows that the system of equations can describe the growth of a single bacterial cell.

Goodwin (1970) has studied the case of many cells simultaneously growing and applied the statistical mechanical techniques described earlier in this paper to an ensemble of oscillators, each oscillator controlling the growth of one cell.

Lastly, we mention a model of an optical maser (Lamb, 1964) in which the intensities of various modes satisfy the Volterra's equation with the Verhulst term, with the exception that the interaction matrix a_{ij} is symmetric.[4] In deriving the equations, Lamb considers a high-Q multimode cavity in which there is a given *classical* electromagnetic field which acts on a collection of two-level atoms described by the laws of *quantum* mechanics. The macroscopic electric polarization

---

[4] We are thankful to Dr. H. M. Nussenzveig for bringing to our attention this theory of optical masers.

produced by the electromagnetic field is taken to be the source for the electromagnetic field in accordance with Maxwell's equations. The self-consistent calculations then yield the amplitudes and frequencies of the possible oscillations. For a two-mode maser, the intensities I_1 and I_2 of the two modes satisfy the equations

$$\dot{I}_1 = 2I_1(\alpha_1 - \beta_1 I_1 - \theta_{12} I_2), \qquad (9.11a)$$

$$\dot{I}_2 = 2I_2(\alpha_2 - \beta_2 I_2 - \theta_{21} I_1), \qquad (9.11b)$$

where α_1, α_2, β_1, β_2, θ_{12}, and θ_{21} are certain parameters in the model. α_1 is the net single-pass unsaturated gain and is simply related to the negative absorption coefficient of the medium at frequencies of mode 1. $\beta_1 I_1$ is the decrease in that net gain due to saturation (population depletion) of the gain curve by mode 1, and $\theta_{12} I_2$ is the decrease in the gain due to saturation by mode 2. α_2, β_2, and $\theta_{21} I_1$ have similar meanings. Some discussions of the equations (9.11a) and (9.11b) is given in Lamb (1964) and Fork and Pollack (1965).

For a laser with N modes above the threshold of oscillation, the differential equations describing the competition among the modes are of the form

$$\tfrac{1}{2}\dot{I}_n = (\alpha_n - \beta_n I_n) I_n - \sum_{\substack{m \neq n \\ 1}}^{N} \theta_{mn} I_m I_n,$$

where I_n is a measure of the intensity of mode n, α_n is the over-all gain resulting from the balance of pumping and losses, β_n is a saturation parameter representing the decrease in gain due to the depletion of population inversion, and $\theta_{mn} = \theta_{nm}$ is the interaction coefficient between modes m and n.

No statistical mechanical treatment of the several-mode optical maser has been done. However, considerable attention has been given to the noise in masers and lasers. The resulting Fokker–Planck equation has been studied, both analytically and numerically. For details of the equation and the solutions, we refer the readers to two recent reviews (Louisell, 1969; Haken, 1970).

XI. Experimental Verification of Volterra's Model

In this section we will describe some of the experiments which throw light on the validity of Volterra's model. The relevant experiments fall into two categories. In the first category, we have observations in a natural ecological system which may provide some evidence for the model. In the second category are the controlled experiments which have been specifically designed to test the model through its predictions. An excellent and exhaustive review of the experiments and their connection with Volterra's model is given by D'Ancona (1954). We will give, in the following, only a sampling of these experiments.

In the first category we have the classic investigations by D'Ancona (1926) on the fish populations of the Upper Adriatic which inspired Volterra to his detailed study. Among other things, what D'Ancona observed was that there was an optimum in the intensity with which fishing is exercised. When the intensity is diminished below a certain limit, the more voracious species are more numerous than others, and when this optimum is exceeded, there is a reduction in numbers in both groups of species. This is in accordance with Volterra's model, for, from (1.1), the steady state population of two species in a prey–predator system is

$$q_1 = \alpha_2/\lambda_2, \qquad q_2 = \alpha_1/\lambda_1.$$

Removing both species in quantities proportional to their numbers is equivalent to increasing α_2 and decreasing α_1 and, therefore, q_1; hence, the number of individuals of the first species (prey) will increase while those of the second (predator) will decrease.

However, if the intensity is large enough to make α_1 negative, then the number of individuals of both species will decrease. (Volterra called the above conclusion the Law of the Disturbance of the Averages.)

Volterra's theory for many species implies that if the number of species is large, the fluctuations are not periodic. The data collected 1924–1942 by Elton and his collaborators at the Bureau of Animal Populations in Oxford on the rodents and fur animals of the northern regions of America (Elton, 1942) support this implication. Probably, physical environmental factors contribute to some extent to these fluctuations, but it is also obvious from these experiments that interactions between various species contribute significantly to these fluctuations.

A spectacular verification of the law of disturbance of averages is provided in the field of insecticides. This is quoted in MacArthur and Connell (1966). The cottony cushion scale insect (*Icerya purchasi*) was accidentally introduced from Australia in 1868 and threatened to destroy the American citrus industry. To counteract this, its natural Australian predator, a ladybird beetle, *Novius cardinalis*, was introduced. This kept the scale to a low level. When DDT was discovered to kill scale insects, it was applied by the orchardists in the hope of further reducing the scale insects. However, in agreement with the above principle, the effect was an increase of the scale insect itself.

In the second class, Gause (1934, 1935) was the earliest worker to do extensive experiments on prey–predator systems in laboratories in order to test Volterra's model. He was particularly interested in the maintenance of oscillatory systems and this he was able to achieve on a number of occasions. In none of the experiments quoted in his book (Gause, 1934) was this possible without arranging for small daily additions at a regular rate of one or the other of the species. This was regarded by Gause as immigration. The apparent contradiction with Volterra's model is generally explained by the fact that the number of animals present was too small to avoid accidental extinction of one or another species. However, in the experiments (Gause, 1935) on *Paramecium bursaria* feeding on *Saccharomyces pombe* and *P. aurelia* on *S. exiguus*, several complete cycles of oscillation were maintained before extinction occurred.

Next we mention the work done by L'Heritier and Teissier (1935) on mixed cultures of the two species *Drosophila melanogaster* and *Drosophila funebris*, which have the same food requirement and obtain food from the same sources. A stable equilibrium comes to be formed between them which is independent of the initial proportions of the individuals of each species in the culture. There are fluctuations around the equilibrium level. This is in accordance with Volterra's model for two species which are competing for the same food rather than having a prey–predator relation.

DeBach and Smith (1941) made cultures of the common domestic fly and the species *Mormoniella vitripennis*, which parasitizes the pupae of the fly under controlled environments. They observed fluctuations in the number of individuals of both species, proving that the fluctuations were due to the prey–predator interaction and not to fluctuations in the environment.

Utida (1957) and his collaborators have carried out complex work on the host–parasite population of Azuki bean weevil and its parasitic wasp. They have shown that the interacting populations of host and parasite exhibit cyclic fluctuations from generation to generation, but that with advancing generations, the intensity of fluctuation diminishes. This slow settling down to equilibrium is just what we expect from Volterra's model when the Verhulst term is present.

We should make mention of the very good account of the interplay of theory and experiment, as described in Neyman, Park, and Scott (1956). There they discuss the experiments of Park and his collaborators on the flour beetle *Tribolium*. The main result was that the repetition of the experiment many times over long periods showed that the outcome of a particular competition situation, beginning with certain definite proportion of the two species in a fixed amount of flour medium, is not rigidly fixed but is subject to statistical probability. These experiments point to the need of introduction of stochastic processes in the theory.

Finally we turn to the analysis of data to verify the statistical aspects of Volterra's theory. Leigh (1969) has made two such analyses. First he analyzed the data of Huffaker (1957), who created a prey–predator oscillation in the laboratory using a prey mite feeding on oranges and another species of mite as its predator. Using the random noise theory, Leigh calculated the various coefficients in the equation through the use of autocorrelation functions. Two points are of interest. First, the Verhulst term is comparable to the interaction term. Second, he theoretically obtained a period of 100 days, which compares not unfavorably with the observed period of 70 days. He made a similar analysis of the catches of Canadian lynx and its primary food, the varying hare. He detected oscillation through the use of autocorrelation function which changed sign with time. Here also the Verhulst terms are comparable to other terms which reflect crowding effect. However, his theoretically computed period of 25 years is very far from the observed period of 10 years. This leads him to believe that the oscillation must have a different cause.

Kerner (1959) has made a statistical analysis of the data on catches of fox by the Moravian missions in Labrador from 1834 to 1925 as compiled by Elton (1942) to check his hypothesis about the canonical distribution. He computes the value of Θ from various averages on the fox-catch data and finds a reasonably uniform value, which is a test of the canonical hypothesis. He then uses the data to calculate the frequency of crossing of zero by the variable $v = \log N/q$. His theoretical results compare not unfavorably with the experimental results. While this is hardly a justification of the theory, it gives some idea of the validity of statistical mechanics in Volterra's system.

Appendix A: TIME AVERAGES OF VARIOUS FUNCTIONS OF N_i AND $\dot{N}_i$

In this appendix we will first calculate the time averages of various functions of N_i and $\dot{N}_i$ for a two-species system directly by using the dynamical equations (1.2). We will then use the same method for calculating the time averages of some corresponding functions for a many-species system and, also, for deriving the equations satisfied by the time averages of other functions.

Equations (1.2) for two-species system are

$$dN_i/dt = k_1 N_1 + \beta_1^{-1} a_{12} N_1 N_2, \qquad \text{(A1a)}$$

$$dN_2/dt = k_2 N_2 + \beta_2^{-1} a_{21} N_1 N_2. \qquad \text{(A1b)}$$

Using (1.6), we can write these equations as

$$dv_1/dt = (1/\beta_1) a_{12} y_2, \qquad \text{(A2a)}$$

$$dv_2/dt = (1/\beta_2) a_{21} y_1, \qquad \text{(A2b)}$$

where

$$y_i = N_i - q_i, \qquad i = 1, 2, \qquad \text{(A3a)}$$

$$v_i = \ln (N_i/q_i), \qquad i = 1, 2. \qquad \text{(A3b)}$$

We have already shown in Sec. 1 that

$$[\![N_i]\!] = q_i, \qquad \text{(A4a)}$$

i.e.,

$$[\![y_i]\!] = 0. \qquad \text{(A4b)}$$

To calculate $[\![N_1 N_2]\!]$, we take the time average of (A1a) to obtain

$$a_{12}[\![N_1 N_2]\!] = -k_1 \beta_1 [\![N_1]\!] = -k_1 \beta_1 q_1 \qquad \text{(A5)}$$

which, when (1.6) is used

$$[\![N_1 N_2]\!] = q_1 q_2 \qquad \text{(A6)}$$

or, from (A3) and (A4),

$$[[y_1 y_2]] = 0. \tag{A7}$$

To calculate $[[N_1{}^2]]$, we note that due to the anti-symmetry of a_{12} from (A1a) and (A1b),

$$\beta_1 \dot{y}_1 + \beta_2 \dot{y}_2 = k_1 \beta_1 y_1 + k_2 \beta_2 y_2. \tag{A8}$$

Therefore, we have

$$d(\beta_1 y_1 + \beta_2 y_2)^2/dt = 2(\beta_1 y_1 + \beta_2 y_2)(k_1 \beta_1 y_1 + k_2 \beta_2 y_2).$$

Taking time average of both sides and using (A7), we find

$$k_1 \beta_1 [[y_1{}^2]] + k_2 \beta_2 [[y_2{}^2]] = 0. \tag{A9}$$

Since, from (1.6), we have

$$k_1 \beta_1 q_1 + k_2 \beta_2 q_2 = 0, \tag{A10}$$

Eq. (A9) gives

$$\beta_1 [[y_1{}^2]]/q_1 = \beta_2 [[y_2{}^2]]/q_2 \equiv \theta_2 \tag{A11}$$

or

$$[[N_i{}^2]] = q_i{}^2 + \theta_2(q_i/\beta_i), \qquad i = 1, 2, \tag{A12}$$

where θ_2 is a constant. We now calculate the time averages of cubic functions of N_i's. From (A1a) we have

$$d(\beta_1 N_1{}^2)/dt = 2[k_1 \beta_1 N_1{}^2 + a_{12} N_1{}^2 N_2]. \tag{A13}$$

Taking the time average of both sides and using (1.6), we find

$$a_{12}([[N_1{}^2 N_2]] - [[N_1{}^2]] q_2) = 0,$$

i.e.,

$$[[N_1{}^2 N_2]] = [[N_1{}^2]] q_2 \quad \text{or} \quad [[y_1{}^2 y_2]] = 0. \tag{A14}$$

In general, since

$$d(\beta_1 [[N_1{}^p]])/dt = p[k_1 \beta_1 N_1{}^p + a_{12} N_1{}^p N_2], \tag{A15}$$

taking the time average of this equation and using (1.6), we get

$$\llbracket N_1{}^p N_2 \rrbracket = \llbracket N_1{}^p \rrbracket q_2 \quad \text{or} \quad \llbracket y_1{}^p y_2 \rrbracket = 0, \qquad p \text{ integer.}$$

$$(A16)$$

To calculate $\llbracket N_1{}^3 \rrbracket$, we follow the procedure used for the calculation of $\llbracket N_1{}^2 \rrbracket$ to get

$$k_1 \beta_1{}^3 \llbracket N_1{}^3 \rrbracket + k_2 \beta_2{}^3 \llbracket N_2{}^3 \rrbracket = 0$$

which, together with (A10), gives

$$\beta_1{}^2 \llbracket y_1{}^3 \rrbracket / q_1 = \beta_2{}^2 \llbracket y_2{}^3 \rrbracket / q_2 \equiv \theta_3, \quad \text{a constant} \quad (A17)$$

or

$$\llbracket N_1{}^3 \rrbracket = \llbracket N_1{}^2 \rrbracket q_1 + 2\theta_2 (q_1{}^2/\beta_1) + \theta_3 (q_1/\beta_1{}^2). \quad (A18)$$

To calculate $\llbracket N_1{}^2 N_2{}^2 \rrbracket$, we take the time average of the identity

$$d(N_1{}^2 N_2)/dt = 2 N_1 N_2 \dot{N}_1 + \dot{N}_2 N_1{}^2$$

$$= (2k_1 + k_2) N_1{}^2 N_2 + (a_{21}/\beta_2) N_1{}^3 N_2$$

$$+ (2/\beta_1) a_{12} N_1{}^2 N_2{}^2.$$

If we use (A16) and (1.6), the resulting equation simplifies to

$$\llbracket N_1{}^2 N_2{}^2 \rrbracket = \llbracket N_1{}^2 \rrbracket q_2{}^2 + (\beta_1/2\beta_2) q_2 (\llbracket N_1{}^3 \rrbracket - q_1 \llbracket N_1{}^2 \rrbracket).$$

$$(A19)$$

By using (A12) and (A18), we further simplify the above equation to

$$\llbracket N_1{}^2 N_2{}^2 \rrbracket = \llbracket N_1{}^2 \rrbracket q_2{}^2 + (\theta_2 q_2/\beta_2) [q_1{}^2 + (\theta_3/2\theta_2)(q_1/\beta_1)]$$

$$(A20a)$$

which can be written as

$$\llbracket y_1{}^2 y_2{}^2 \rrbracket = (\theta_3/2)(q_1 q_2/\beta_1 \beta_2). \qquad (A20b)$$

To calculate $\llbracket N_1{}^4 \rrbracket$ we use the same method as used for calculating $\llbracket N_1{}^2 \rrbracket$ and $\llbracket N_1{}^3 \rrbracket$. On doing so we find

$$\beta_1{}^3[y_1{}^4 - \tfrac{3}{2}(q_1{}^2/\beta_1{}^2)\theta_3]/q_1 = \beta_2{}^3[[y_2{}^4]] - \tfrac{3}{2}(q_2{}^3/\beta_2{}^2)\theta_3]/q_2$$

$$= \theta_4, \quad \text{a constant} \quad (A21)$$

which can be used to calculate $[[N_1{}^4]]$.

From the above discussion it is clear that if we know $[[N_1{}^p]]$, we can calculate $[[N_2{}^p]]$ and $[[N_1{}^p N_2{}^q]]$.

Let us now calculate the time averages involving v_1, v_2, and their time derivatives. Since, from (A2a), we have

$$d(v_1{}^2)/dt = 2v_1 a_{12} y_2/\beta_1,$$

when we take the time average, we get

$$[[v_1 y_2]] = 0.$$

However, since from (A2) we have

$$(d/dt)(v_1 v_2) = (a_{12}/\beta_1)v_2 y_2 - (a_{12}/\beta_2)v_1 y_1, \quad (A22)$$

$$\beta_1[[v_1 y_1]] = \beta_2[[v_2 y_2]] = \phi_2, \quad \text{a constant.} \quad (A23)$$

Also, from Eq. (A2), we have

$$[[\dot{v}_1]] = 0, \quad (A24a)$$

$$[[\dot{v}_1 v_2]] = (a_{12}/\beta_1)[[y_2 v_2]] = a_{12}\phi_2/\beta_1\beta_2, \quad (A24b)$$

$$[[\dot{v}_1 y_1]] = (a_{12}/\beta_1)[[y_1 y_2]] = 0, \quad (A24c)$$

$$[[\dot{v}_1 y_2]] = (a_{12}/\beta_1)[[y_2{}^2]] = a_{12}\theta_2 q_2/\beta_1\beta_2, \quad (A24d)$$

$$[[\dot{v}_1 \dot{v}_2]] = (a_{12}/\beta_1)[[\dot{v}_2 y_2]] = 0, \quad (A24e)$$

$$[[\dot{v}_1{}^2]] = (a_{12}/\beta_1)[[\dot{v}_1 y_2]] = a_{12}{}^2\theta_2 q_2/\beta_1{}^2\beta_2, \quad (A24f)$$

$$[[d^2 v_1/dt^2]] = 0. \quad (A24g)$$

Using (A1), (A2), (A23), and (A24), we can calculate all the averages of polynomials involving v_1 and v_2 and their time derivatives.

To calculate the time averages for a many-species system, we follow the same procedure as for a two-species system. Taking the time average of (1.2), we get

$$0 = k_i[[N_i]] + (1/\beta_i)\sum_j a_{ij}[[N_i N_j]]$$

which, using (1.18) and (1.6), becomes

$$\sum_j a_{ij}(\llbracket N_i N_j \rrbracket - q_i q_j) = 0 \qquad \text{(A25a)}$$

or

$$\sum_j a_{ij}\llbracket y_i y_j \rrbracket = 0. \qquad \text{(A25b)}$$

Equation (A25b) is a set of n equations, one for each i, involving n^2 variables $\llbracket y_i y_j \rrbracket$ $(i=1, \cdots, n; j=1, \cdots, n)$ and thus represents an undetermined set. A solution consistent with (A25b) is

$$\llbracket y_1 y_j \rrbracket = 0. \qquad \text{(A26)}$$

To calculate $\llbracket N_i^2 \rrbracket$ we note that

$$\frac{d}{dt}(\sum_{i=1}^n \beta_i y_i)^2 = 2(\sum_{k=1}^n \beta_k y_k)\sum_{i=1}^n \beta_i \dot{y}_i. \qquad \text{(A27)}$$

But from (1.2), due to the antisymmetry of a_{ij}, we have

$$\sum_{i=1}^n \beta_i \dot{y}_i = \sum_{i=1}^n k_i \beta_i y_i. \qquad \text{(A28)}$$

Substituting (A28) into (A27), and taking the time average, we find

$$\sum_{i,k} k_i \beta_i \beta_k \llbracket y_i y_k \rrbracket = 0 \qquad \text{(A29)}$$

or

$$\sum_i k_i \beta_2{}^2 \llbracket y_i{}^2 \rrbracket + \sum_{\substack{i,k \\ i \neq k}} k_i \beta_i \beta_k \llbracket y_i y_k \rrbracket = 0. \qquad \text{(A30)}$$

If we assume that (A26) is true, then this equation becomes

$$\sum_i k_i \beta_i{}^2 \llbracket y_i{}^2 \rrbracket = 0. \qquad \text{(A31)}$$

Since in this equation there are n variables, we cannot solve for the variables $\llbracket y_i{}^2 \rrbracket$. However, since from (1.6)

$$\sum k_i \beta_i q_i = 0, \qquad \text{(A32)}$$

we conclude that

$$\beta_i[\![y_i{}^2]\!]/q_i = \theta_2, \qquad \text{a constant}, \qquad (A33)$$

is a solution of (A31). If we extend the procedure to calculate the time averages of high powers of N_i, we continue to find an underdetermined set of equations. However, it can be easily seen that if

$$[\![N_1{}^{p_1}N_2{}^{p_2}\cdots N_n{}^{p_n}]\!] = [\![N_1{}^{p_1}]\!][\![N_2{}^{p_2}]\!]\cdots[\![N_n{}^{p_n}]\!]$$

is assumed to be true, then

$$[\![y_i{}^p]\!] = (p-1)(\theta_2/\beta_i)([\![y_i{}^{p-1}]\!]+q_i[\![y_i{}^{p-2}]\!]),$$

$$i = 1, 2, \cdots, n, \quad (A34)$$

is consistent with the equations for the time averages of various functions of N_i's.

Appendix B: MICROCANONICAL AVERAGES
OF VARIOUS FUNCTIONS OF N_i

In this appendix, we will calculate the microcanonical averages of various functions of N_i for a many-species system. The basic formula which we use is given in Sec. 1 [Eq. (1.29)], i.e.,

$$E\{f\} = \int_{G(0)} fds/|\nabla G| \,\bigg| \int_{G(0)} ds/|\nabla G|, \qquad \text{(B1)}$$

where ds is an element of area on a surface of constant G, the surface integral area over the surface $G=G(0)$, and

$$\nabla G = \sum_i (\partial G/\partial v_i)\hat{v}_i, \qquad \text{(B2)}$$

where $\hat{v}_i$ is a unit vector in the v_i direction. To calculate $E\{f\}$, we write f as a derivative of G and substitute in (B1). Let us first calculate the microcanonical ensemble averages of the following functions:

$$f_1 = y_i = (N_i - q_i) = \beta_i^{-1}(\partial G/\partial v_i), \qquad \text{(B3a)}$$

$$f_2 = (N_i - q_i) \ln (N_i/q_i) = \beta_i^{-1}v_i(\partial G/\partial v_i), \qquad \text{(B3b)}$$

$$f_3 = y_i y_j = (\beta_i\beta_j)^{-1}(\partial G/\partial v_i)(\partial G/\partial v_j). \qquad \text{(B3c)}$$

Since

$$\frac{\partial G}{\partial v_i} \bigg/ |\nabla G| = \hat{n}\cdot\hat{v}_i, \qquad \text{(B4)}$$

where $\hat{n}$ is a unit vector normal to the surface $G=$ constant, we have

$$\int f_1 \frac{dS}{|\nabla G|} = \beta_i^{-1} \int \hat{n}\cdot\hat{v}_i \, ds = \beta_i^{-1} \int \nabla\cdot\hat{v}_i \, d\tau = 0.$$

$$\text{(B5a)}$$

APPENDIX B

To obtain the last integral, we have used the Gauss divergence theorem. Thus we have

$$E\{f_1\} = 0, \quad \text{i.e.,} \quad E\{y_1\} = 0. \qquad (B5b)$$

Similarly, we have

$$\int f_2 ds / |\,\boldsymbol{\nabla} G\,| = \beta_i^{-1} \int v_i \hat{n} \cdot \hat{v}_i \, ds$$
$$= \beta_i^{-1} \int \boldsymbol{\nabla} \cdot v_i \, d\tau = \beta_i^{-1} \int d\tau \equiv \tau_0/\beta_i, \qquad (B6)$$

where τ_0 is the volume enclosed by $G(0)$, and

$$\int f_3 ds / |\,\boldsymbol{\nabla} G\,| = (\beta_i \beta_j)^{-1} \int (\partial G/\partial v_i) \hat{n} \cdot \hat{v}_i \, ds$$
$$= (\beta_i \beta_j)^{-1} \int (\partial/\partial v_i)(\partial G/\partial v_j) \, d\tau$$
$$= 0 \qquad\qquad \text{if } i \neq j$$

$$\qquad\qquad\qquad\qquad\qquad\qquad (B7a)$$

$$= (1/\beta_i^2) \int (\partial^2 G/\partial v_i^2) \, d\tau \qquad \text{if } i = j.$$

$$(B7b)$$

Thus we find

$$E\{y_i y_j\} = 0 = E\{x_i x_j\}, \qquad \text{if } i \neq j. \qquad (B8a)$$

By extending the proof of (B8a), one can easily show that

$$E\{x_{i_1} x_{i_2} \cdots x_{i_n}\} = 0, \qquad \text{if } i_1 \neq i_2 \neq \cdots \neq i_n, \quad (B8b)$$
$$E\{x_{i_1} x_{i_2}{}^{p_2} \cdots x_{i_n}{}^{p_n}\} = 0, \qquad \text{if } i_1 \neq i_2, \cdots \neq i_n. \quad (B8c)$$

To calculate $E[y_i^2]$, we note that from (1.9a)

$$\partial^2 G/\partial v_i^2 = \partial^2 G_i/\partial v_i^2 = (\partial G_i/\partial v_i) + q_i \beta_i = (\partial G/\partial v_i) + q_i \beta_i.$$

$$(B9)$$

Therefore, from (B7b), we have

$$\int y_i^2 ds / |\,\boldsymbol{\nabla} G\,| = (q_i/\beta_i)\tau_0 + (1/\beta_i^2) \int (\partial G/\partial v_i) \, d\tau. \quad (B10)$$

But we also have

$$\int (\partial G/\partial v_i) \, d\tau = \int \boldsymbol{\nabla} \cdot G\hat{v}_i \, d\tau = \int G\hat{n} \cdot \hat{v}_i \, ds$$
$$= G\int \hat{n} \cdot \hat{v}_i \, ds = G\int \boldsymbol{\nabla} \cdot \hat{v}_i \, ds = 0. \quad (B11)$$

Therefore, (B10) becomes

132

$$\int y_i^2 ds/|\ \nabla G\ | = (q_i/\beta_i)\tau_0$$

$$= q_i \int y_i \ln\ (N_i/q_i)\, ds/|\ \nabla G\ |, \quad \text{(B12)}$$

where τ_0 is the volume enclosed by the surface $G = G(0)$. Therefore, we have

$$E\{y_i^2\} = q_i E\{y_i \ln\ (N_i/q_i)\}. \quad \text{(B13)}$$

Further, if we write

$$\frac{\tau_0}{\int ds/|\ \nabla G\ |} \equiv \theta_2, \quad \text{(B14)}$$

$$E\{y_i^2\} = (q_i/\beta_i)\theta_2, \quad \text{(B15a)}$$

$$E\{y_i \ln\ (N_i/q_i)\} = \theta_2/\beta_i, \quad \text{(B15b)}$$

Eq. (B15a) for the microcanonical average is consistent with (A31) for the time average.

To calculate the average of y_i^3, we extend the proof of (B7b) to get

$$\int y_i^3\, \frac{ds}{|\ \nabla G\ |} = \frac{1}{\beta_i^3} \int \frac{\partial}{\partial v_i} \left(\frac{\partial G}{\partial v_i}\right)^2 d\tau$$

which, when (B9) is used, becomes

$$\int y_i^3 ds/|\ \nabla G\ |$$

$$= (2/\beta_i^3)\left[\int (\partial G/\partial v_i)^2\, d\tau + q_i\beta_i \int (\partial G/\partial v_i)\, d\tau\right]$$

$$= (2/\beta_i^3) \int (\partial G/\partial v_i)^2\, d\tau. \quad \text{(B16)}$$

To evaluate the integral on the right-hand side, we note that

$$\int (\partial G/\partial v_i)^2\, d\tau = \int \nabla \cdot (\partial G/\partial v_i)^2 v_j\, d\tau \quad j \text{ arbitrary}, j \neq i,$$

$$= \int (\partial G/\partial v_i)^2 v_j (\partial G/\partial v_j)\, ds/|\ \nabla G\ | \quad \text{(B17)}$$

which can further be written as

$$\int (\partial G/\partial v_i)^2\, d\tau = \int \hat{n} \cdot [v_j(\partial G/\partial v_j)(\partial G/\partial v_i)]\hat{v}_i\, ds$$

$$= \int v_j(\partial G/\partial v_j)(\partial^2 G/\partial v_i^2)\, d\tau$$

$$= q_i\beta_i \int v_j(\partial G/\partial v_j)\, d\tau. \quad \text{(B18)}$$

133

Since j was arbitrary, the integral on the right-hand side of j in the above equation should be independent of j. Therefore, from (B16) and (B18), we have

$$E\{y_i{}^3\} = (q_i/\beta_i{}^2)\theta_3, \qquad (B19)$$

where

$$\theta_3 = 2! \int v_j \frac{\partial G}{\partial v_j}\, d\tau \Big/ \int \frac{ds}{|\nabla G|}. \qquad (B20)$$

Proceeding in a similar fashion, one can show that

$$E\{y_i{}^4\} = (3q_i/\beta_i{}^3)[\theta_4/3 + q_i\beta_i\theta_3/2] \qquad (B21a)$$

or

$$\frac{\beta_i{}^3[E(y_i{}^4) - \tfrac{3}{2}(q_i{}^2/\beta_i{}^2)\theta_3]}{q_i} = \theta_4, \qquad (B21b)$$

where

$$\theta_4 = 3! \int v_j \frac{\partial G}{\partial v_j} v_k \frac{\partial G}{\partial v_k}\, d\tau \Big/ \int \frac{ds}{|\nabla G|}. \qquad (B22)$$

This procedure can be generalized to calculate the average of $N_i{}^p$. Let us now evaluate $E\{y_i{}^2 y_j{}^2\}$. Using the procedure followed for calculating $E\{y_i{}^2\}$, and using (B9), one can show that

$$\int y_i{}^2 y_j{}^2 ds / |\nabla G|$$
$$= (\beta_i{}^2\beta_j{}^2)^{-1}[\int (\partial G/\partial v_i)^2\, d\tau + q_i\beta_i \int (\partial G/\partial v_j)^2\, d\tau].$$

Since the first integral vanishes, using (B18) and (B20), one finds that the above equation becomes

$$E\{y_i{}^2 y_j{}^2\} = \tfrac{1}{2}(q_i/\beta_i)\beta_j E\{y_j{}^3\}$$
$$= \tfrac{1}{2}(q_i q_j/\beta_i\beta_j)\theta_3. \qquad (B23)$$

The above procedure can be generalized to calculate $\{y_i{}^p y_j{}^q\}$. It may be noted that if we know $E\{N_i{}^p\}$ for each p and i, we can calculate $E\{N_1{}^{p_1}N_2{}^{p_2}\cdots N_n{}^{p_n}\}$.

If

$$E\{y_i{}^2 y_j{}^2\} = E\{y_i{}^2\}E\{y_j{}^2\},$$

then from (B23) and (B15a), we have

$$\theta_3 = 2!\theta_2{}^2.$$

In general, if we demand that

$$E\{y_1{}^{p_1}y_2{}^{p_2}\cdots y_n{}^{p_n}\} = E\{y_1{}^{p_1}\}E\{y_2{}^{p_2}\}\cdots E\{y_n{}^{p_n}\},$$

then all the θ's and, hence, all the microcanonical averages, can be expressed in terms of θ_2.

Appendix C: CANONICAL AVERAGES OF VARIOUS FUNCTIONS OF N_i, v_i, AND THEIR TIME DERIVATIVES

In this appendix, we will derive the expressions for the canonical averages of various functions of N_i, v_i, $\dot{v}_i$, dv_1^2/d^2t, etc.

The basic equation which we use is (1.35), i.e.,

$$\langle f \rangle = \frac{\int f \exp\,(-G_\nu/\Theta)\;d\tau}{\int \exp\,(-G_\nu/\Theta)\;d\tau}\,, \qquad (C1)$$

where $\langle f \rangle$ denotes the canonical average of a function f. Since, from (1.9a),

$$y_i = N_i - q_i = \beta_i^{-1}(\partial G/\partial v_i),$$

we have

$$\langle y_i \rangle = \beta_i^{-1}[\int (\partial G/\partial v_i)$$
$$\times \exp\,(-G_i/\Theta)\;dv_i/\int \exp\,(-G_i/\Theta)\;dv_i]$$
$$= -(\Theta/\beta_i)[\int (\partial/\partial v_i)$$
$$\times [\exp\,(-G_i/\Theta)]\;dv_i/\int \exp\,(-G_i/\Theta)\;dv_i]$$
$$= -(\Theta/\beta_i)[(\exp\,\{-\beta_i q_i$$
$$\times [\exp\,(v_i)-v_i]\})_{-\infty}^{\infty}/\int \exp\,(-G_i/\Theta)\;dv_i]$$

or

$$\langle y_i \rangle = 0. \qquad (C2)$$

The average of y_i^2 is given by

$$\langle y_i^2 \rangle = (-\Theta/\beta_i^2)[\int (\partial G/\partial v_i)(\partial/\partial v_i)$$
$$\times [\exp\,(-G_i/\Theta)]\;dv_i/\int \exp\,(-G_i/\Theta)\;dv_i].$$

Integrating the integral in the numerator by parts, we get

$$\langle y_i^2 \rangle = (\Theta/\beta_i^2)[\int (\partial^2 G/\partial v_i^2)$$

$$\times \exp\left(-G_i/\Theta\right) dv_i / \int \exp\left(-G_i/\Theta\right) dv_i]$$

which, when (B9) is used, reduces to

$$\langle y_i{}^2 \rangle = (\Theta q_i/\beta_i) + (\Theta/\beta_i{}^2)\langle \partial G/\partial v_i \rangle = \Theta q_i/\beta_i. \quad (C3)$$

Extending the above calculations for $\langle y_i{}^p \rangle$, we get

$$\langle y_i{}^p \rangle = (\Theta/\beta_i{}^p)(p-1)[\int (\partial G/\partial v_i)^{p-2}(\partial^2 G/\partial v_i{}^2)$$

$$\times \exp\left(-G_i/\Theta\right) dv_i / \int \exp\left(-G_i/\Theta\right) dv_i]$$

which, when (B9) is used, reduces to

$$\langle y_i{}^p \rangle = (\Theta/\beta_i)(p-1)[\langle y_i{}^{p-1} \rangle + q_i\langle y_i{}^{p-2} \rangle]. \quad (C4)$$

Also, we have

$$\langle y_i \ln\left(N_i/q_i\right)\rangle = \beta_i{}^{-1}\langle v_i(\partial G/\partial v_i)\rangle$$

$$= \{-\Theta/\beta_i[v_i \exp\left(-G_i/\Theta\right)]_{-\infty}{}^{\infty}$$

$$+ (\Theta/\beta_i)\int \exp\left(-G_i/\Theta\right) dv_i\}/\int \exp\left(-G_i/\Theta\right) dv_i$$

$$= \Theta/\beta_i = \langle y_i{}^2 \rangle/q_i. \quad (C5)$$

As pointed out in Sec. 1, because of the decomposibility of G into its component, i.e., $G = \sum_i G_i$,

$$\langle f_1(y_1)f_2(y_2)\cdots f_n(y_n)\rangle = \langle f_1(y_1)\rangle\langle f_2(y_2)\rangle\cdots\langle f_n(y_n)\rangle. \quad (C6)$$

Equations (C2), (C3), (C4), and (C6) can be used to calculate canonical average of any polynomial function of N_i.

To calculate the averages of polynomials in v_i (Kerner, 1959), we note that from (C1) and (1.9a),

$$\langle \exp\left(\lambda v_i\right)\rangle = \frac{\displaystyle\int_{-\infty}^{\infty} \exp\left(\lambda v_i\right) \exp\left\{-x_i[\exp\left(v_i\right) - v_i]\right\} dv_i}{\displaystyle\int_{-\infty}^{\infty} \exp\left\{-x_i[\exp\left(v_i\right) - v_i]\right\} dv_i}$$

$$= x_i{}^{-\lambda}\left(\int_0^{\infty} t^{\lambda + x_i - 1}e^{-t}\, dt \Big/ \int_0^{\infty} t^{x_i - 1}e^{-t}\, dt\right)$$

or

$$\langle \exp (\lambda v_i) \rangle = \Gamma(\lambda + x_i)/\Gamma(x_i) x_i^{-\lambda}. \quad (C7)$$

The averages of polynomials in v_i can be calculated by repeated differentiation of (C7) with respect to λ and then letting $\lambda \to 0$. For example, we find

$$\langle v_i \rangle = (\partial/\partial\lambda) \langle \exp (\lambda v_i) \rangle = \phi(x_i) - \ln x_i, \quad (C8)$$

$$\langle v_i^2 \rangle = \phi'(x_i) + [\phi(x_i) - \ln x_i]^2, \text{ etc.}, \quad (C9)$$

where ϕ is the digamma function and ϕ' is the trigamma function.

The averages of polynomials involving derivatives can be calculated by using Eq. (1.8), i.e.,

$$\beta_i \dot{v}_i = \sum_j a_{ij} q_j [\exp (v_j) - 1]$$

$$= \sum_j a_{ij} y_j = \sum_j [a_{ij}(1/\beta_j)(\partial G/\partial v_j)]. \quad (C10)$$

Taking canonical averages of both sides and using (C2), we get

$$\langle \dot{v}_i \rangle = 0. \quad (C11)$$

Further, since

$$\beta_i (dv_i^2/dt^2) = \sum_j a_{ij} q_j \exp (v_j) \dot{v}_j$$

and since $\dot{v}_j$ is independent of v_j, we find

$$\langle dv_i^2/dt^2 \rangle = 0. \quad (C12)$$

As pointed out by Kerner (1959), the averages of quantity like $v_k \dot{v}_i$ can be used to observe the microscopic parameter a_{ij}/β_i of the Volterra's equation. This can be seen by multiplying (C10) by v_k and taking the averages of both sides of the equation, i.e.,

$$\beta_i \langle v_k \dot{v}_i \rangle = \sum_j a_{ij} \langle y_j v_k \rangle$$

$$= a_{ik} \langle y_k v_k \rangle \quad (C13)$$

which, when (C5) is used, becomes

$$\langle v_k \dot{v}_i \rangle = a_{ik}\Theta/\beta_i\beta_k. \quad (C14)$$

139

APPENDIX C

When (C3) is used, this equation transforms to

$$a_{ik}/\beta_i = \langle \dot{v}_i v_k \rangle / q_k \langle y_k^2 \rangle \qquad (C15)$$

which is the required equation for calculating a_{ik}/β_i by measuring N_i and N_k as a function of time. Averages of other functions of v_i and its time derivatives can be calculated by procedures similar to the one described above.

Appendix D: ROOTS OF THE EQUATION
$$ze^z + \gamma = 0, \quad \gamma \text{ COMPLEX}$$

In this appendix, we will derive the condition for which the real parts of all the roots of the above equation, i.e., of equation

$$ze^z + \rho e^{i\theta} = 0, \qquad \gamma = \rho e^{i\theta}, \qquad \rho, \theta \text{ real}, \qquad \text{(D1)}$$

are negative. If we make the substitution

$$\xi = z - i\theta, \qquad \text{(D2)}$$

Eq. (D1) becomes

$$H(\xi) \equiv \xi e^{\xi} + i\theta e^{\xi} + \rho = 0. \qquad \text{(D3)}$$

Since Re (z) = Re (ξ), the conditions for Re (z) or Re (ξ) to be less than 0 are identical. To find these conditions we use a theorem (13.7) from Bellman and Cooke (1963). According to this theorem, let $H(\xi) = h(\xi, e^{\xi})$ be a polynomial with a principal term[5] and $H(iy) = F(y) + iG(y)$. If all the zeros of the function $H(\xi)$ lie to the left side of the imaginary axis, then the zeros of the functions $F(y)$ and $G(y)$ are real, alternating,[6] and

$$G'(y)F(y) - G(y)F'(y) > 0 \qquad \text{(D4)}$$

for each y. Moreover, in order that all the zeros of the function lie to the left of the imaginary axis, it is sufficient that one of the following conditions be satisfied:

---

[5] The term $a_{ij}x^i y^j$ of the polynomial $\sum_{m,n} a_{mn} x^m y^n$, m, n non-negative, is called the principal term if for each $a_{mn} x^m y^n$ with $a_{mn} \neq 0$, we have either $i > m, j > n$ or $i = m, j > n, i > m, j = n$.

[6] That is, between two roots of $F(y)$ there is a root of $G(y)$, and vice versa.

(a) All the zeros of $F(y)$ and $G(y)$ are real and alternate, and inequality (D4) is satisfied for at least one value of y.

(b) All the zeros of $F(y)$ are real and, for *each* zero $y = y_0$, inequality (D4) is satisfied.

(c) Same as (b), except for $G(y)$.

For the function $H(\xi)$ given by (D3), we have

$$F(y) = \rho - (y + \theta) \sin y, \qquad \text{(D5a)}$$

$$G(y) = (y + \theta) \cos y. \qquad \text{(D5b)}$$

The zeros of $G(y)$ are

$$y_0 = -\theta, \qquad \text{(D6a)}$$

$$y_0 = \pm(n + \tfrac{1}{2})\pi, \qquad n = 0, 1, \cdots, \qquad \text{(D6b)}$$

and, for these roots,

$$G'(y_0)F(y_0) = \rho \cos \theta = \mathrm{Re}\,(\gamma), \qquad \text{(D7a)}$$

$$G'(y_0)F(y_0) = (-1)^n[(n+\tfrac{1}{2})\pi \pm \theta]$$
$$\times [(-1)^n\{(n+\tfrac{1}{2})\pi \pm \theta\} - \rho]. \qquad \text{(D7b)}$$

If $\mathrm{Re}\,(\gamma) \leq 0$, condition (D4) is not satisfied, at least for $y = y_0 = -\theta$, and, therefore, the real parts of all the roots of Eq. (D1) are not less than 0. For $\mathrm{Re}\,(\gamma) > 0$, $-\pi/2 < \theta < \pi/2$, and $(n+\tfrac{1}{2})\pi \pm \theta > 0$. Therefore, from Eqs. (D7a) and (D7b) and (b) of the above theorem, for $\mathrm{Re}\,(\gamma) > 0$, we find real parts of all the roots of (D1) < 0 provided

$$\tfrac{1}{2}\pi \pm \theta > \rho,$$

i.e.,

$$\tfrac{1}{2}\pi - |\theta| > \rho, \qquad \gamma = \rho e^{i\theta}. \qquad \text{(D8)}$$

For $\theta = 0$, i.e., $\gamma = \rho$, the above condition reduces to $\tfrac{1}{2}\pi > \rho$, which is equivalent to the condition (8.19).

References

D'Ancona, U., 1926, R. Comit. Talass. *It.* Mem. **126**, 95.
——, 1954, *The Struggle for Existence* (Brill, Leiden).
Bak, T., 1963, *Contributions to the Theory of Chemical Kinetics* (Benjamin, New York).
Bellman, R., and K. L. Cooke, 1963, *Differential-Difference Equations* (Academic, New York).
——, H. Kagiwada, and R. Kalaba, 1966, J. Theoret. Biol. **11**, 164.
Caianiello, E. R., 1959, Nuovo Cimento Suppl. **14**, 177.
Chiang, C. L., 1954, in *Statistics and Mathematics in Biology*, edited by O. Kempthorne, T. A. Bancroft, J. W. Gowen, and J. L. Lush (Iowa State College Press, Ames, Iowa), p. 197.
Cowan, J. D., 1968, in *Neural Networks*, edited by E. R. Caianiello, (Springer, New York), p. 181.
Cunningham, W. J., 1954, Proc. Natl. Acad. Sci. U.S. **40**, 709.
——, 1955, Bull. Math. Biophys. **17**, 101.
Davis, H. T., 1941, *Theory of Econometrics* (Principia Press, Bloomington, Ind.), Chap. 11.
De Bach, P., and H. S. Smith, 1941, Ecology **22**, 363.
Dunkel, G., 1968, in *Seminar on Differential Equations and Dynamical Systems*, edited by Jones, G. S. (Springer, New York).
Elton, C., 1942, *Voles, Mice, and Lemmings* (Oxford U. P., London).
Ford, J., 1961, J. Math. Phys. **2**, 387.
——, and J. Waters, 1963, J. Math. Phys. **4**, 1293.
Fork, R. L., and M. A. Pollack, 1965, Phys. Rev. **139**, A1408.
Garfinkel, D., 1962, Nature **194**, 856.
——, 1965, in *Theoretical and Mathematical Biology*, edited by T. H. Waterman and H. J. Morowitz (Blaisdell, New York).
——, 1967a, J. Theoret. Biol. **14**, 46.
——, 1967b, J. Theoret. Biol. **14**, 325.
Gause, G. F., 1934, *The Struggle for Existence* (Williams and Wilkins, Baltimore).
——, 1935, Verifications Experimentales de la theory mathematique de la lutte pour la vie; Actualités Sci. et Ind. No. 277.
Gause, G. F., and A. A. Witt, 1935, Am. Naturalist **69**, 596.
Glass, D. V., 1967, Proc. Roy. Soc. (London) **B168**, 119.
Gompertz, B., 1825, Phil. Trans. Roy. Soc. **115**, 513.
Goodwin, B. C., 1963, *Temporal Organization in Cells* (Academic, New York).
——, 1970, J. Theoret. Biol. **28**, 375.
Haken, H., 1970, "Laser Theory," Handbuch der Physik, edited by S. Flügge (Springer, New York), Vol. 25, Part 2c.
Halanay, A., 1966, *Differential Equations, Stability, Oscillations*,

143

REFERENCES

Time Lags (Academic, New York).

L'Heritier, Ph., and G. Teissier, 1935, Compt. Rend. Soc. Biol. **118**, 1396.

Higgins, J., 1967, Ind. Eng. Chem. (Intern. Edition) **59**, 19.

Huffaker, C. B., 1957, Hilgardia **27**, 343.

Hutchinson, G. E., 1947, Ecology **28**, 319.

Jones, G. S., 1961, Proc. Natl. Acad. Sci. U. S. **47**, 879.

Kac, M., 1943, Am. J. Math. **65**, 609.

Kakutani, S., and L. Markus, 1958, in *Contribution to the Theory of Nonlinear Oscillations*, edited by S. Lefschetz (Princeton U. P., Princeton, N. J.).

Kerner, E. H., 1957, Bull. Math. Biophys. **19**, 121.

——, 1959, Bull. Math. Biophys. **21**, 217.

——, 1961, Bull. Math. Biopys. **23**, 141.

——, 1971, *Gibbs Ensemble; Biological Ensemble* (Gordon & Breach, New York).

Khinchin, A. I., 1959, *Mathematical Foundations of Statistical Mechanics* (Dover, New York).

King, C. E., and G. J. Paulik, 1967, J. Theoret. Biol. **16**, 251.

Kostitzin, V. A., 1939, *Mathematical Biology* (George G. Harrap, London).

Kryloff, N., and N. Bogoliuboff, 1947, *Introduction of Non-linear Mechanics* (Princeton U. P., Princeton, N. J.).

Lamb, W. E., Jr., 1964, Phys. Rev. **134**, A1429.

Lefever, R., G. Nicolis, and I. Prigogine, 1967, J. Chem. Phys. **47**, 1045.

Leigh, E. G., Jr., 1965, Proc. Natl. Acad. Sci. U. S. **53**, 777.

——, 1969, in *Some Mathematical Problems in Biology*, edited by M. Gerstenhaber (American Mathematical Society, Providence, R. I.).

Levin, J. J., 1965, Proc. Am. Math. Soc. **16**, 711.

——, 1969, J. Diff. Equations **5**, 369.

Louisell, W. H., 1969, in *Quantum Optics*, edited by R. J. Glauber (Academic, New York), p. 680.

Lotka, A. J., 1910, J. Phys. Chem. **14**, 271.

——, 1920, Proc. Natl. Acad. Sci. U. S. **6**, 410.

——, 1956, *Elements of Mathematical Biology* (Dover, New York).

MacArthur, R. H., 1955, Ecology **36**, 533.

——, and J. H. Connell, 1966, *The Biology of Populations* (Wiley, New York).

Mazur, P., and E. W. Montroll, 1960, J. Math. Phys. **1**, 70.

Montroll, E. W., 1961, in *Lectures in Theoretical Physics*, edited by W. E. Brittin, B. W. Downs, and J. Downs (Interscience, New York).

——, 1964, in *Applied Combinatorial Mathematics*, edited by E. F. Beckenbach (Wiley, New York), p. 96.

——, 1968, in *Lectures in Theoretical Physics*, edited by A. O. Barut and W. E. Brittin (Gordon and Breach, New York), Vol. XA, p. 531.

Neyman, J., T. Park, and E. L. Scott, 1956, *Proceedings of the Third Berkeley Symposium of Mathematical Statistics and Probability*, edited by J. Neyman (University of California Press, Berkeley), Vol. 4, p. 41.

Nicolis, G., 1970, "Stochastic Analysis of the Volterra–Lotka Model," unpublished.

Pearl, R., 1924, *Studies in Human Biology* (Williams and Wilkins, Baltimore).

Pearl, R., and L. J. Reed, 1920, Proc. Natl. Acad. Sci. U. S. **6**, 275.

Pennycuick, C. J., R. M. Compton, and L. Beckingham, 1968, J. Theoret. Biol. **18**, 316.

Pinney, E., 1958, *Ordinary Difference-Differential Equations* (University of California Press, Berkeley).

Preston, F. W., 1969, in *Diversity and Stability in Ecological Systems*, edited by G. M. Woodwell and H. H. Smith (Brookhaven National Laboratory, Upton, L. I.).

Rescigno, A., 1968, Bull. Math. Biophys. **30**, 291.

——, and I. W. Richardson, 1967, Bull. Math. Biophys. **29**, 377.

Richardson, L. F., 1960, in *Arms and Insecurity*, edited by N. Rashvesky and E. Trucco (Quadrangle Books, Chicago).

Slater, N. B., 1939, Proc. Camb. Phil. Soc. **35**, 56.

Slobodkin, L. B., 1961, *Growth and Regulation of Animal Populations* (Holt, Rinehart, and Winston, New York).

Smith, J. M., 1969, *Mathematical Ideas in Biology* (Cambridge U. P., London).

Titchmarsh, E. C., 1937, *Introduction to the Theory of Fourier Integrals* (Clarendon, Oxford).

Trischka, J., and H. Salwen, 1959, J. Chem. Phys. **31**, 218.

Utida, S. C., 1957, Cold Spring Harbor Symp. **22**, 139.

Utz, W. R., and P. E. Waltman, 1963, Bull. Math. Biophys. **25**, 75.

Verhulst, P. F., 1845, Nuov. Mem. Acad. Roy. Bruxelles **18**, 1; see, also, **20**, 1 (1847).

Volterra, V., 1928, J. Conseil Permanent Intern. Exploration Mer III, 1; translated in *Animal Ecology*, by R. N. Chapman (McGraw-Hill, New York, 1931).

——, 1931, *Lecon sur la theorie mathematique de la lutte pour la vie* (Gauthier-Villars, Paris).

——, 1937, Acta Biotheoret. **3**, 1.

Waltman, P. E., 1964, Bull. Math. Biophys. **26**, 39.

Wang, M. C., and G. E. Uhlenbeck, 1945, Rev. Mod. Phys. **17**, 323.

Wangersky, P. J., and W. J. Cunningham, 1957, Ecology **38**, 136.

Wintner, A., 1933, Am. J. Math. **55**, 309.

Woodwell, G. M., and H. H. Smith (Eds.), 1969, *Diversity and Stability in Ecological Systems* (Brookhaven National Laboratory, Upton, L. I.).

Woolley, W. H., 1970, J. Theoret. Biol. **28**, 305.

——, and A. G. De Rocco, 1970, Biophys. J. **10**, 183.

Wright, E. M., 1955, J. Reine Angew. Math. **194**, 66.

——, 1959, Bull. Am. Math. Soc. **65**, 89.